MO
CROSSWORDS

1st SHOWING

Thomas Trickett

Publications Ltd

Thomas Trickett

Publications Ltd

First published in 1997
by THOMAS TRICKETT PUBLICATIONS LTD
4 Harrison Avenue, Bournemouth
BH1 4NT, UK

Film Consultant and Researcher:
Owen Llewellyn BA(Hons)

ISBN 0 9524483 3 5

Typesetting and cover by Poole Typesetting
(Wessex) Limited, Bournemouth, England, UK
Printed by Bishops Printers,
Southsea, Hampshire, England, UK

Acknowledgements

Yet again we express our thanks to the
Thomas Trickett team but we give a special
mention to Nuala Alys who inspired us all

Thomas Trickett Publications Ltd

Foreword

For several years, I have compiled
crosswords on sporting subjects.

Now, for the enjoyment of cinema-goers
and home-viewers everywhere, here is my
crossword book on movies.

Good Luck,

Thomas Trickett

DOORS
OPEN

1

Across

1. French meeting gives title of William Powell 1935 movie (10)
8. Residence site completes title of film: ". . . . . . Unknown" (7)
9. ". . . . . A Hot Tin Roof" (1958) (3 & 2)
10. Always; occurs twice in "Never Say Never Again" (4)
11. Over 'toot' for Dorothy's dog in "The Wizard of Oz" (4)
12. "The Railway Children" holds what sicken us (3)
14. Swindle – as Topol did "on the Roof"? (6)
15. Oscar . . . . . .'. "The Ideal Husband" was made into a film (6)
18. Jar reversed for era when the film "The Drum" was set (3)
20. "Helen of . . . .", 1955 Italian film of classical heroine (4)
21. Time period between each Academy Award ceremony (4)
23. Film title: "Shakespeare Wallah" conceals Moslem deity (5)
24. Rap game up for title of Mitchum 1963 movie (7)
25. Mike Leigh's 1996 Palme D'Or winner – ". . . . . Lies" (7 & 3)

Down

1. Dared he change Lucille Ball's hair-colour? (7)
2. Enthralling movies . . . . well-written plots (4)
3. "Give us tonight's cinema tickets" hides London station (6)
4. English Queen (1837–1901) whom Sybil Thorndike has played (8)
5. Sam Peckinpah films were known for being . . . . . - violent (5)
6. Chief British film censor for many years (5 & 6)
7. Where was Wes Craven's "Nightmare"? (2, 3, 6)
13. Full surname of Chevy Chase's character in "Fletch" (8)
16. Explosive 1988 Bruce Willis movie (3 & 4)
17. Hercule, Agatha Christie's Belgian detective (6)
19. Ms. Andrews, singing star of "The Sound of Music" (5)
22. Mame altered for Jane Austen-inspired film (4)

Across

1. Film: "Up Periscope" conceals range (5)
4. Foxtrot or tango for "White Mischief" actor Charles (5)
10. Grouse conceals what thrilling films do to your emotions (5)
11. Shakespeare's Moor played by Laurence Fishburne (7)
12. Roy, leading actor in the smash hit "Jaws" (8)
13. Slang for a dollar or John Candy comedy: "Uncle . . . ." (4)
15. German city for "Easter Parade" composer Irving? (6)
17. Luc, French director of "Leon" (6)
19. Bogart's character in "Casablanca" (4)
20. Hunting a change for title of 1963 film, "The . . . ." (8)
23. Double Arnie's character for pencil rubbers? (7)
24. Part of editing room upon which discarded film is left (5)
25. An . . . . . film is not meant for children (5)
26. If risky films are made, they can conceal a police search (5)

Down

2. Settee completes film title: "The . . . . . Trip" (1988) (5)
3. The Spanish army rank for Peter Hyams film of 1988 (8)
5. Flashy film productions hide quality of fiery remains (4)
6. "Three . . . . : Blue" (1993) (7)
7. Emeric, film-making partner of Michael Powell (11)
8. Bee-product needed for when "I Shrunk the Kids" (5)
9. Actress Melanie Griffith's industrious female (7 & 4)
14. . . . . Jason Leigh, acted up in "Single White Female" (8)
16. Style of music in Elvis films: '. . . . . . . Roll' (4 & 3)
18. Sean Connery film: "Just . . . . ." (1995) (5)
21. Metal golf clubs bring you to English film actor Jeremy (5)
22. Ringing name for "Wish You Were Here" actor, Tom? (4)

Across
1. Sandy shoreline areas for Hershey/Midler film (1988) (7)
7. Superman is "The Man of . . . . ." (A metal) (5)
8. Female performer; one who acts (7)
9. War film: "The . . . . . . on the River Kwai" (1957) (6)
11. Spencer Tracy film ". . . . . Who's Coming to Dinner" (1967) (5)
13. Steven Spielberg's take on the Peter Pan story (4)
14. Disaster movie: "The Towering . . . ." (1974) (7)
15. Richard, co-starred in "Pretty Woman" (4)
16. John Grisham novel turned into film: "The Pelican . . . ." (5)
17. ". . . . . . Goes By" 1987 Australian comedy (2 & 4)
21. Evil Len change for John who was Baron Munchausen (1989) (7)
22. The pain going with "The Ecstasy" for Michelangelo biopic (5)
23. Anthony, author of "A Clockwork Orange" (7)

Down
2. Hit movie – "Close . . . . of the Third Kind" (10)
3. Julie, English actress, appeared in the movie "Dragonheart" (8)
4. Sale over for "Bride of Frankenstein", Ms. Lanchester (4)
5. Night sky twinkler for film ". . . . dust Memories" (1980) (4)
6. Not alive like the "Poets Society"? (4)
9. Director Sonnenfeld – or Kubrick's "Lyndon" (5)
10. DeNiro, Pesci and Liotta collectively (1990) (10)
12. On a film set, a foreman hides old term for in front (5)
13. Wooden structure on which film posters are stuck (8)
18. Roman gown worn, for example, in the film "Caligula" (4)
19. Small British car – star of "The Italian Job" (4)
20. Bill of fare – in the movie "Diner", perhaps? (4)

Across

1. Shortened version of actor Mr. Olivier's first name (5)
7. Sylvester, first hit the big time with "Rocky" (8)
8. Film which parodies Rambo: "Hot . . . . .!: Part Deux" (5)
10. School where George Cole played Flash Harry (2 & 8)
12. ". . . . . Dragon" – Bruce Lee film (5 & 3)
14. Film actor – Charles Grodin – hides a Viking god (4)
16. & 23 Across. Principal actor in "Midnight
    Express" (4 & 5)
17. Industrial action for Bruce Willis: ". . . . . Distance"? (8)
20. French director who married Brigitte Bardot and
    Jane Fonda (5 & 5)
23. See 16 Across.
24. Nationality of Richard Gere's 1980 "Gigolo" (8)
25. Glossy surface to "Wall Street" Charlie? (5)

Down

1. Charles lies down, hiding comedy star Mr. Nielsen's
   name (6)
2. Terrifying type of rodents seen in "Ben" (1972) (4)
3. One of plenty in Hollywood or in night sky (4)
4. Quickly close then open eyes for Madeleine Stowe film (5)
5. Willem Dafoe/Miranda Richardson 1994 film (3, 3, 3)
6. Liam, played leading Irish republican Michael Collins (6)
9. Disney tale – "Toy . . . . ." (5)
11. Shocking movie for its time: "The Boston
    . . . ." (1968) (9)
13. The opposite to a flop of a movie (3)
15. A Robert Davi video hides distinct quality of some films (5)
16. Occupation of Tom Cruise's character in "Cocktail" (6)
18. Mel, film actor, first seen in the "Mad Max" movies (6)
19. Brian over – Woody Allen's "second favourite organ" (5)
21. ". . . ., poor Yorrick, I knew him Horatio." – Hamlet (4)
22. Robert Altman's satire on the Korean/Vietnam war
    (1970) (4)

Across

6. Richard, actor/director – maker of "Gandhi" (12)
8. Underwater missile fired in War movies (7)
9. "The Tall Guy" conceals eighth letter of Greek alphabet (5)
10. Change of Lino for "Romeo is Bleeding" Lena (4)
12. Ma's lab reversed for movie actor Martin (6)
14. Sophia, glamorous Italian actress from the Sixties (5)
15. Larry, T.V.'s 'J.R.', son of Mary Martin, in many films (6)
16. Group of actors and actresses in a film (4)
19. Here digressions in films can hide further use of spade (5)
21. A law has changed for "In the Bleak Midwinter" Julia (7)
22. How many marriages go with "a Funeral"? (4 & 8)

Down

1. British money for 'Keystone Kops' actor, Ford? (8)
2. Derisive remark critic makes about least-liked film (5)
3. Type of racing – as seen in 1966 film "Grand Prix" (5)
4. The deliverer of mail who "Always Rings Twice" (7)
5. A Guest Star in T.V.-movie hides shivery fever (4)
6. Schwarzenegger film: "Last . . . ." (6 & 4)
7. "One Hundred and One" of these dogs in movie (10)
11. Relationship of Michael Douglas to Kirk (3)
12. Actor Ed Begley Jr.'s name conceals to plead earnestly (3)
13. Sylvester, of "Cliffhanger" fame (8)
14. Lillie, shown in "The Life and Times of Judge Roy Bean" (7)
17. Arthur, music-hall comic, starred in "The Ghost Train" (5)
18. A vegetable for Greta Garbo's nationality? (5)
20. Fall for Wesley Snipes's parachuting in ". . . . Zone"? (4)

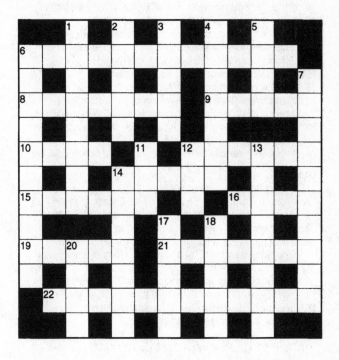

Across

3. Area of New York for Woody Allen movie (9)
8. Nave reversed for screenwriter, Mr. Hunter (4)
9. Place for budgerigar in title of Robin Williams' film? (8)
10. Has "Sleepwalkers" concealed trouble? (6)
13. Mr. Wise, Morecambe's partner, in "That Riviera Touch" (5)
14. Mexican drink for title of film: ". . . . . . . Sunrise" (7)
15. Robert Wise directed boxing film: "The . . . Up" (3)
16. Condition you might get if sound in cinema is too loud (7)
17. Meat on human body for Warhol 'underground' film (5)
21. Can certain films contain a sign of the Zodiac? (6)
22. Mishap which might befall characters in "The Hospital"? (8)
23. John Barrymore played the Latin lover "Don . . . ." (1926) (4)
24. Musical assemblage who perform grand film-scores (9)

Down

1. Paul, director of "Basic Instinct" (9)
2. Richard Harris film: "The . . . . Crossing" (1976) (9)
4. Actor Buster Crabbe yelled inside a religious building (5)
5. Girl's name for movie: ". . . . . . . Craig" (1950) (7)
6. The Friar in the "Robin Hood" movies (4)
7. Special gathering in Tinseltown hides form of plankton (4)
11. Keaton, Hawn and Midler film: "First . . . ." (5 & 4)
12. Ms. Ross, the object of attention in "The Graduate" (9)
14. Kind of shirt Brando wore in "The Wild One" (3)
15. Shakes with cold for David Cronenberg Horror movie? (7)
18. Person delivering lines on screen (5)
19. Mark on Al Pacino in ". . . . face" (1983) (4)
20. "When You . . . . Upon A Star" – song from "Pinocchio" (4)

Across

1. "The Bad . . . ." – controversial Harvey Keitel film (10)
8. 'United . . . .' film co., started by Chaplin and others (7)
9. Mated changed for Shakespeare's "Shrew" at film's end? (5)
10. "Leon" turned for the multi-talented Mr. Coward's name (4)
11. Brave man for "Local . . . ." (1983) (4)
12. "Dead On Arrival" – in short, for movie title (3)
14. Jodie, whose directorial debut was "Little Man Tate" (6)
15. Richard Harris film: "A Man . . . . . . Horse" (6)
18. Michelle Pfeiffer was . . . woman in "Batman Returns" (3)
20. Pursuit of a habit contains "Moby Dick" captain (4)
21. Ms. Thompson who was in "Peter's Friends" (4)
23. "The Hunchback of . . . . . Dame" (5)
24. Change red pole for how moralists view risqué flicks (7)
25. U.S. actress – danced with Travolta in "Pulp Fiction" (3 & 7)

Down

1. Romantic epistles in "Love . . . ." (1945) (7)
2. Name of the lion cub in the film "Born Free" (4)
3. One who samples food or what a trailer gives of a movie (6)
4. & 16 Down. ". . . . .'s Animal House" (8 & 7)
5. Wandering tribesman for Brosnan's 1985 flick: ". . . . .s" (5)
6. Sort of "Seven" led by Yul Brynner in Western (11)
7. The Fox brothers/actors' first names (eldest first) (6 & 5)
13. Coloured warning going out when film-spies break in (3 & 5)
16. See 4 Down.
17. April and August conceal film actor Martin's name (6)
19. Child-star daughter of Ryan O'Neal (5)
22. Star, Ms. Pamela Anderson, contains meaty product (4)

7

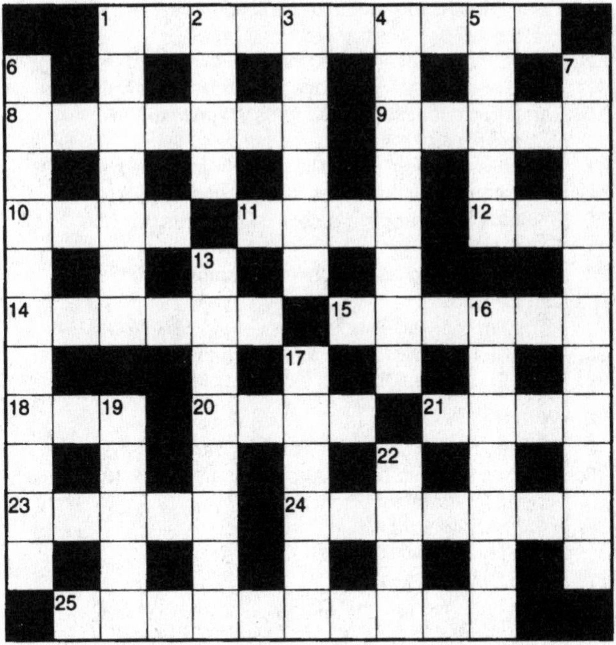

Across
1. Witty Irish playwright Mr. Wilde played by Robert Morley (5)
4. Rock-hard "Sliver"-actress Sharon? (5)
10. Where "Talk Radio" speech goes out (2 & 3)
11. Reach above your head for 1960 comedy: "Two Way
. . . ." (7)
12. Actor Charles Boyer played this French military genius (8)
13. Patrick Stewart's "Star" voyage at the movies? (4)
15. Large lizard for Richard Burton's "Night of the
. . . . . ." (6)
17. The assassination, in the film "J.F.K.", happened here (6)
19. Tool returned for Joe Orton's filmed comedy (4)
20. Shirley, was Streep's mother in "Postcards from the
Edge" (8)
23. Should Hoffman have worn a mackintosh for this
part? (4 & 3)
24. 1971 film of Dylan Thomas play: ". . . . . Milk Wood" (5)
25. "Unlawful . . . . ." (1992) Ray Liotta movie (5)
26. Does the movie "McVicar" hide man of the cloth? (5)

Down
2. Postage sticker for British film actor Terence? (5)
3. Hilarious send-up of the "Airport" disaster films (8)
5. Ripped "Curtain" for Hitchcock film? (4)
6. & 7 Down. Violent film starring Woody
Harrelson (7 & 4, 7)
7. See 6 Down.
8. Tosca changed for what Robbie Coltrane is (1 & 4)
9. Original writer behind Ian McKellen's "Richard III" (11)
14. Up Alumni changed for star of "Scarface" (1932) (4 & 4)
16. "You top Ian's acting" – hiding "Lost Horizon" world (7)
18. Canonization for the Val Kilmer movie character? (5)
21. "A Passage to . . . . ." (1984) (5)
22. Film: "The Miracle" hides male issue of Muhammad (4)

Across

1. "The . . . ."; Burt Lancaster's aquatic sportsman (7)
7. Peter, who played the monster in "Young Frankenstein" (5)
8. Sidney, played the teacher in "To Sir with Love" (7)
9. Early Tom Hanks film where he met a fishy Daryl Hannah (6)
11. Ms. Winger, starred in "Shadowlands" (5)
13. ". . . . Is the Hunter" (1964) Disaster movie (4)
14. U.S. state in Nicolas Cage movie: "Raising . . . ." (7)
15. Deadly weapon-contest for early Spielberg movie (4)
16. Tale – such as Steve Martin's "L.A. . . . . ." (5)
17. Name of asylum in Karloff movie (1946) (6)
21. Pierce, James Bond actor (7)
22. Actor George C., sounds like one from Caledonia (5)
23. Jason, was Capone in "The St. Valentine's Day Massacre" (7)

Down

2. Comedy/musical: "The Best Little . . . . in Texas" (10)
3. Tram Lane for instinct missing in "Mommie Dearest"? (8)
4. Do cinema multiplexes conceal former lovers? (4)
5. "There's a Girl in My . . . ." – Peter Sellers film (4)
6. Help Lean's movie to contain a fervent request (4)
9. Neil, writer behind many Matthau/Lemmon films (5)
10. Film actor Kiefer, son of Donald (10)
12. Mini movie-maker conceals a musical note (5)
13. Disney film where Mickey Mouse used sorcery (8)
18. ". . . . Soup" – Marx Brothers' picture (4)
19. Timothy Dalton's surname hides a singing voice (4)
20. Type of group such as the 'Three Stooges' (4)

Across

1. "Star Trek III: The Search for . . . . ." (1984) (5)
7. Ms. Dalle, took the lead role in French movie "Betty Blue" (8)
8. Actor Jerry, abducted by Rupert Pupkin in "The King of Comedy" (5)
10. Actor, who played bogus doctor in "Paper Mask" (4 & 6)
12. Henry, director of films like "The Sons of Katie Elder" (8)
14. Canines from Tarantino's "Reservoir"? (4)
16. The film "Beethoven" covers stove (4)
17. Unfortunate mishap for title of Dirk Bogarde 1967 film (8)
20. Denzel, actor in the film "Philadelphia" (10)
23. David, actor who wrote "Bring on the Empty Horses" (5)
24. The film "Anzio" deals with the 1944 . . . . in Italy (8)
25. Maclaine and Nicholson's were "of Endearment" (5)

Down

1. Ron Howard directed this funny mermaid movie (6)
2. A film excerpt shown on a T.V. movie programme (4)
3. Not Heaven for British Horror movie: ". . . . raiser" (4)
4. Robert, T.V.'s Eliot Ness, appeared in the movie "Airplane" (5)
5. Dark, sultry actress from "Angel Heart" (4 & 5)
6. Walter Matthau film about a 'Menace' of a child (6)
9. The Devil in a Bette Davis film: ". . . . . Met a Lady" (5)
11. Barbra, singer/actress who was in "What's Up, Doc?" (9)
13. Car change for powerful studio-lighting lamp (3)
15. Paul Sorvino played Henry Kissinger in this Stone film (5)
16. George, author of "1984", which was turned into a movie (6)
18. Sport Farley Granger played in "Strangers on a Train" (6)
19. All night observance fans keep after film idol's death (5)
21. Leslie Caron and Louis Jourdan were in this 1958 musical (4)
22. Ustinov was Poirot in the film "Death on the . . . ." (4)

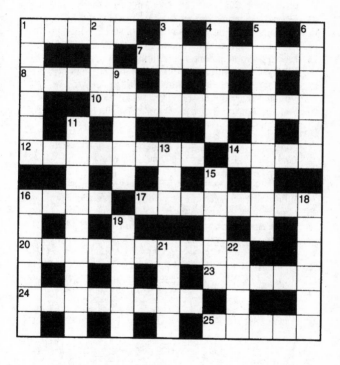

Across

6. "Trainspotting" star appeared in "Brassed Off" (4 & 8)
8. Spencer Tracy film: ". . . . . . . the Wind" (7)
9. Heart-throb Clark, was in 1935 "Mutiny on the Bounty" (5)
10. Robert, British actor who was in "The Hireling" (4)
12. Kidnap money demanded for title of Mel Gibson film (6)
14. Inexperienced colour of John Wayne's "Berets"? (5)
15. Merle, played Catherine in "Wuthering Heights" (1939) (6)
16. Michael, male-sounding director of the film "Heat" (4)
19. Number of "Amigos" in Steve Martin comedy (5)
21. Evening of today for song from "West Side Story" (7)
22. Helena, actress in Trevor Nunn's "Twelfth Night" (6 & 6)

Down

1. "Billy . . . ." – Dustin Hoffman gangster movie (8)
2. Change Mr. Eye for comic Dick, who was in "Baby Love" (5)
3. ". . . . . kick out of you" sung by Astaire in film (1, 3, 1)
4. Ingrid, actress who married Roberto Rossellini (7)
5. Hair accessory not needed by Yul Brynner (4)
6. He plunged syringe into Uma in "Pulp Fiction" (4 & 6)
7. A rotten rim changed for Arnie's robotic humanoid (10)
11. The film "Saturn Three" conceals a cremation vase (3)
12. Colour of Nicolas Cage's movie – ". . . Rock West" (3)
13. Tara gets jumbled for James Spader sci-fi flick (8)
14. ". . . . with . . . Wind" – film of Margaret Mitchell book (4 & 3)
17. Chop 'Forre G' off "Forrest Gump" for felled-tree remains (5)
18. Comic actor James Finlayson hides inset pattern (5)
20. Mob disorder as in movie – ". . . . in Cell Block Eleven" (4)

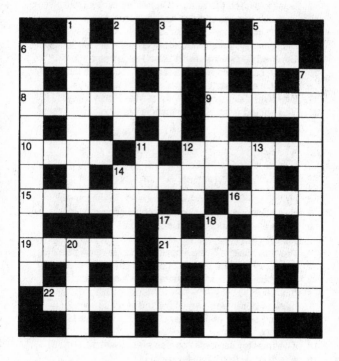

Across

3. Wild individual like "Conan"? (9)
8. Vex a movie critic, hiding a written test (4)
9. Susan, played the nun in "Dead Man Walking" (8)
10. In Westerns, the Indians send message by smoke . . . . . . (6)
13. Ms. Winfrey, who appeared in "The Color Purple" (5)
14. Southern U.S. state for William Holden film-title (7)
15. British comic Mr. Mayall was Toad in cartoon film (3)
16. Tom Cruise film: "Days of . . . ." (1990) (7)
17. War film: ". . . . . of Iwo Jima" (1949) (5)
21. You should . . . . . . your film ticket to prove you have paid (6)
22. Movie of Henry James novel: "The . . . . of a Lady" (8)
23. Leg-joint for Eric Rohmer's film: "Claire's . . . ." (4)
24. Rudolph, 1920s romantic screen idol (9)

Down

1. Barry Sonnenfeld version of Elmore Leonard novel (3 & 6)
2. Unsafe – like Michelle Pfeiffer movie: ". . . . . Minds" (9)
4. Area of church "The Father of the Bride" walks up? (5)
5. Go crazy – as in the title of a Joan Crawford movie (7)
6. Actor George Brent's name hides weekly housing payment (4)
7. Type of bomb seen in a Tom and Jerry cartoon? (4)
11. Film on source of the Nile – ". . . . . of the Moon" (9)
12. Traveller on transport for film: ". . . . . 57" (9)
14. The movie "Staircase" contains what we breathe (3)
15. A further writing of a film script (7)
18. Sixties playwright Joe, subject of "Prick Up Your Ears" (5)
19. Film production and finishing hides a Scottish isle (4)
20. "Babe" pigsty encloses an eye inflammation (4)

Across

1. She played snake stripper in "From Dusk to Dawn" (5 & 5)
8. "Twenty Thousand . . . . under the Sea" (1954) (7)
9. Sugary Mike Leigh film: "Life is . . . . ."? (5)
10. Alfred Hitchcock has poultry in name (4)
11. Weird – ending lost for "Fearless" director, Peter (4)
12. You'd use this currency in a Japanese cinema (3)
14. Carefree quality for Noel Coward's ". . . . . . Spirit"? (6)
15. Jungle animal-hunt for Victor Mature's 1956 movie (6)
18. Cinema is a visual . . . (3)
20. Mr. Schrader, screenwriter of "Raging Bull" (4)
21. Slang for children – title of a raw, adolescent movie (4)
23. Give Tom Conti a rave review; holding a small crown (5)
24. Musical star Jeanette MacDonald's singing voice (7)
25. Seven counters at cinema for paying – hiding meetings (10)

Down

1. Change C.I.C. cash for "The Player" actress, Greta (7)
2. The film title "Brewster McCloud" hasn't a quiet ending (4)
3. Jane, novelist whose "Pride and Prejudice" inspired film (6)
4. Alec Guinness played Hitler; what race was the tyrant? (8)
5. James Cagney played "The Public . . . . ." (1931) (5)
6. Classic horse tale; has been filmed many times (5 & 6)
7. Wants no tins changed for a special effects master (4 & 7)
13. The keyboard instrument for Jane Campion's film? (3 & 5)
16. Dr. Dolittle wished he "could talk to the . . . ." (7)
17. Film actor Rock, appeared many times alongside Doris Day (6)
19. Railway transport for "The . . . . . Robbers" (1973) (5)
22. Fencing sword inside when you see "Peeping Tom"? (4)

Across

1. Like a pig product for unconvincing movie acting? (5)
4. German name for the 1971 Adult cartoon: ". . . . . the Cat" (5)
10. First film-outing for Sigourney Weaver's 'Ripley' (5)
11. Non-professional; like actress in a student film (7)
12. ". . . . . Importance" – Albert Finney picture (1, 3, 2, 2)
13. Hospital room for "Rio Bravo" actor, Mr. Bond (4)
15. Paul, star of "Nobody's Fool" – not an old woman (6)
17. Jamie Lee, "Fierce Creatures" actress (6)
19. A character part in a movie (4)
20. Ingrid Bergman's actress daughter, Ms. Rossellini (8)
23. Sat./Sun. holiday for Jean-Luc Godard film (7)
24. "Twas a miner, forty-. . . . ." "My Darling Clementine" (5)
25. Milo, Irish actor, played Bloom in "Ulysses" (5)
26. "When . . . . . is Born" – Garland/Mason film (1 & 4)

Down

2. Tania changed for film actress Ms. Baker (5)
3. Both genders: "Eat Drink . . . ." (3 & 5)
5. Collective name for the Bob Hope/Bing Crosby films (4)
6. ". . . . . . . of the Mohicans" (3 & 4)
7. U.S. actor, was in "The Best Years of Our Life" (4 & 7)
8. Decorate "Your Wagon" for 1969 Lee Marvin musical (5)
9. Top film dancer was in "Finian's Rainbow" (4 & 7)
14. Male spouses for John Cassavetes 1970 movie (8)
16. Julie, starred in the film "Educating Rita" (7)
18. In Shakespearean films, a remark directed to audience (5)
21. Mario, singing star of "The Great Caruso" (5)
22. Movie of James Jones novel: "From . . . . to Eternity" (4)

Across

1. James, actor who was cooped-up in "Rear Window" (7)
7. Burt Lancaster role: ". . . . . Gantry" (5)
8. The Sixties Pop idols who appeared in "Help!" (7)
9. Darryl F. . . . . . . – "The Grapes of Wrath" producer (6)
11. Mr. Jones who played Toad in "The Wind in the Willows" (5)
13. Filmed Thomas Hardy novel with Nastassja Kinski (4)
14. Connery film: "The Hunt for Red . . . ." (1990) (7)
15. Holy circle above the head of "The Saint"? (4)
16. Film star Elvis changed to reveal wickednesses (5)
17. Full first name of awful director "Ed Wood" (6)
21. Liza Minnelli's singing/acting mother Judy (7)
22. Geena, one half of "Thelma and Louise" (5)
23. Yellow fruit for Woody Allen's South American jaunt (7)

Down

2. Large spotted cat for Visconti's 1963 movie (3 & 7)
3. 1815 Napoleonic disaster gives title of Rod Steiger film (8)
4. Oliver, burly British actor who starred in "Castaway" (4)
5. Jumping insect completes "A . . . . in Her Ear" (1968) (4)
6. Actor Jeff Bridges's brother sounds a dandy (4)
9. Anthony Quinn movie: ". . . . . the Greek" (5)
10. "You must remember this" Bogart movie (1942) (10)
12. Don't sit down for "Custer's Last . . . . ." (1936) (5)
13. Dancing John, who re-emerged in "Pulp Fiction" (8)
18. A wry change for "King Kong" (1933) actress Fay (4)
19. The film "The Runaway Train" ends in wet weather (4)
20. "Ali . . . . and the Forty Thieves" (1954) (4)

Across

1. Items with 5 fingers for film: ". . . . . of the Ripper" (5)
7. ". . . . . Bound: The Incredible Journey" (1993) (8)
8. Running knot in rope needed for "Hang 'em High"? (5)
10. Upper-Scotland dweller for Christopher Lambert fantasy (10)
12. "When Johnny Comes . . . . Home" (1942) movie (8)
14. Warren Beatty's film on the Russian Revolution (4)
16. Family with a common ancestor – relevant to 10 Across? (4)
17. As eleven changed for film comic in "Funny Bones" (3 & 5)
20. Flamboyant Irish playwright played by Stephen Fry (5 & 5)
23. French goodbye for J. Rozier film: ". . . . . Philippine" (5)
24. Thrown out like Amanda Donohue in 1986 film? (8)
25. Herbal name for Sherlock Holmes actor, Mr. Rathbone? (5)

Down

1. Better than some movies; concealing a type of cab (6)
2. Plate you need to receive some satellite movie channels (4)
3. "Mother's Boys" contains clothes-eating, flying insect (4)
4. Taxes altered for the horrifying "Chainsaw Massacre" (5)
5. Bike steering – for moustache-style worn in "Tombstone" (9)
6. Sad roe changes for what a star's fan does to her idol (6)
9. Number of "Seconds" for Luke Perry's rodeo movie title (5)
11. Holly Hunter film on TV news channel: ". . . . . News" (9)
13. Liam Neeson holds woman's pre-married name term (3)
15. Ronald Colman movie: "The Prisoner of . . . . ." (5)
16. Range available for "Sophie's . . . . . ."? (6)
18. A follow-up to a successful film – such as "Speed 2" (6)
19. "Scream and Scream Again" holds double dairy product (5)
21. "I ran the movie for weeks"; hiding new name for Persia (4)
22. Dean changed for Chaplin actress, Ms. Purviance (4)

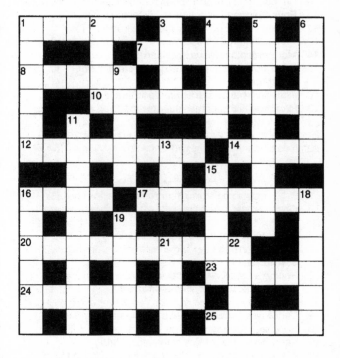

Across

6. "84 . . . . Road" – a David Jones movie (7 & 5)
8. Metal percussion instrument for German film (1979) (3 & 4)
9. Car goes to a Drive-In movie, hiding seaborne goods (5)
10. Boys changed into youths in "A Clockwork Orange" (4)
12. Memory of Schwarzenegger sci-fi movie: "Total
. . . . . ."? (6)
14. Madonna played Eva . . . . . on film (5)
15. Colour of cowardice, often said before movie
gunfights (6)
16. Attractive movie actors are described thus (4)
19. "Somewhere over the Rainbow" has something open
inside (5)
21. A brain's changed for title of Harrison Ford romance (7)
22. Once Mrs. Bogart, she was in the film "Key Largo" (6 & 6)

Down

1. Anthony Hopkins played 'Hannibal-the-. . . . .' (8)
2. . . . . . glycerine is used in movie explosions (5)
3. Chess or Ludo, perhaps, for ". . . . . of Death"
(1945) (1 & 4)
4. Heathland fern for U.S. comic of the Forties, Eddie (7)
5. Type of Russian ruler shown in "Nicholas and
Alexandra" (4)
6. Principal actress in the movie "Mona Lisa" (5 & 5)
7. Beach game with net often seen in California-set films (10)
11. "The Hotel . . . Hampshire", film of a John Irving novel (3)
12. Mr. Steiger, who played Al Capone in 1958 (3)
13. Nationality of George Lucas's 1973 "Graffiti" (8)
14. Large photo's of film stars teenagers hang on walls (7)
17. Walter Lang's "With . . . . . in My Heart" (1952) (1 & 4)
18. What kind of animal is cartoon "Yogi"? (1 & 4)
20. "The Dambusters" conceals Dutch cheese (4)

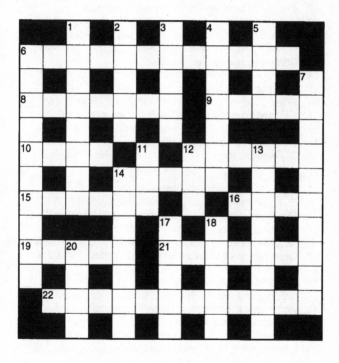

Across

3. Emit flames from mouth for 'planes seen in W.W.II films (9)
8. The film "Striptease" conceals hot beverages (4)
9. Can you believe these in Arnie's 1994 film title? (4 & 4)
10. Pointed projectiles fired by Red Indians in Westerns (6)
13. Outing for fictional agent Jack Ryan: "Patriot . . . . ." (5)
14. Central female subject of a film (7)
15. Paris conceals golfing term quite at home in "Tin Cup" (3)
16. Desirer over what cowboy does when on horse again (7)
17. Willem, played investigator in "Mississippi Burning" (5)
21. Film genre under which "Phantasm" would come (6)
22. John Huston's daughter, who was in "The Grifters" (8)
23. ". . . . Lisa" – Neil Jordan movie (4)
24. "A Streetcar Named Desire" playwright, Mr. Williams (9)

Down

1. ". . . . . on a Train", Hitchcock movie (9)
2. Drew, part of acting dynasty, was young girl in "E.T." (9)
4. Ms. Kensit, actress who appeared in "Lethal Weapon 2" (5)
5. One who strikes, like Bambi's rabbit friend? (7)
6. Lazy-sounding Eric, appears in the Monty Python films (4)
7. Need changes for paradisial-sounding actress, Barbara (4)
11. She played Rosemary in "Rosemary's Baby" (3 & 6)
12. A practice run before camera rolls (9)
14. ". . . Anybody Seen My Girl?" (1952) (3)
15. Anthony, played Norman Bates in "Psycho" (7)
18. Alan Ladd's 1953 Western (5)
19. Horror film "Scanners" conceals a woman's name (4)
20. Jerome, songwriter behind the musical "Showboat" (4)

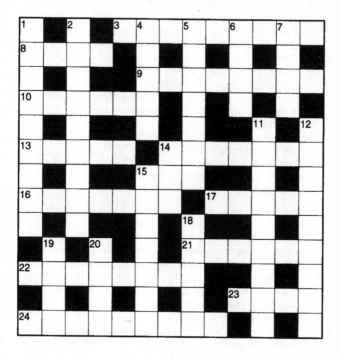

Across

1. Mental tempest for title of Natalie Wood's final film (10)
8. Creepy-crawlies for film: "Angels and . . . ." (7)
9. Nationality of the director, Jim Sheridan (5)
10. James Bond film: "A . . . . to a Kill" (4)
11. Peter, T.V.'s 'Columbo', starred in "Murder by Death" (4)
12. "That'll Be the Day" actor Ringo Starr has a son, name him (3)
14. "Mary . . . . . .", Julia Roberts as Dr. Jekyll's maid (6)
15. Cagney film – ". . . . . . with Dirty Faces" (6)
18. ". . . for Tat" – Hal Roach comedy of 1934 (3)
20. & 13Down. Billy Crystal film about townees on Prairie (4 & 8)
21. Can a creative screenplay contain a measure of land? (4)
23. Elton turned over for "48 Hours"-star, Nick (5)
24. Conspirator, or writer mapping out movie's action (7)
25. "Paris, Texas"-writer/actor; also in "The Right Stuff" (3 & 7)

Down

1. Steve, one of the "Reservoir Dogs" (7)
2. Fredric March's surname hides a semi-circular support (4)
3. Look in "Assault on Precinct 13" for Bahamas capital (6)
4. Slim royal for mental activity aroused by clever films (8)
5. Change of Sizer for Czech director, Karel (5)
6. Alicia, "Clueless"-star, sounds a valuable metal/rock (11)
7. Author of "Twelfth Night" which has been filmed (11)
13. See 20 Across.
16. How you feel when watching a gripping film (7)
17. Just a pleasant film – hiding fastener of pages inside (6)
19. A tail changed for Ms. Shire who was wife of "Rocky" (5)
22. State between life and death for hospital chiller (1978) (4)

Across

1. Shatter – the kind of hit of a big box office success (5)
4. Vagrant; Chaplin's was known as 'The Little . . . . .' (5)
10. Kind of dance-club shown in "Thank God It's Friday" (5)
11. "From Here to Eternity" actress, Ms. Kerr (7)
12. Island prison represented in the movie "The Rock" (8)
13. The film "Climbing High" conceals a leg or arm (4)
15. Vast expanse of sand seen in "Lawrence of Arabia" (6)
17. Taming change for Debbie Reynolds' "The . . . . . .
    Game" (6)
19. "Once . . . . a Time in the West" (1969) (4)
20. Film of Hemingway novel – "A . . . . to Arms" (8)
23. Rare tan changed for what actors do on cartoon films (7)
24. "All Quiet . . . . . Western Front" (2 & 3)
25. African striped horse for movie, "Ice Station . . . . ." (5)
26. Fourteen pounds for "Platoon"-director Oliver? (5)

Down

2. Maurice Jarre got an Oscar for his in "Doctor Zhivago" (5)
3. Preferred modes of transport in "Quadrophenia" (8)
5. Danny Aiello was Jack, Lee Harvey Oswald's killer (4)
6. James Bond's tipple: "Vodka-. . . . . . .; shaken not
   stirred" (7)
7. Writer/director of "The Brothers McMullen" (6 & 5)
8. Star of "Giant" who died young (initial & surname) (1 & 4)
9. The huge doze for Bogart's Philip Marlowe? (3, 3, 5)
14. Without shoes for Jane Fonda – ". . . . . in
    the Park"? (8)
16. Scour Geena Davis's career, hiding punishing whip (7)
18. Alan, wrestled with Oliver Reed in "Women in Love" (5)
21. Mr. John; his "Candle in the Wind" was Marilyn Monroe (5)
22. John Waters camp comedy, ". . . . spray" (4)

Across

1. Country-lover for Harrison Ford's ". . . . . . Games" (7)
7. Leonard, most famous for his portrayal of Mr. Spock (5)
8. Surname of director of "Rumble Fish" (7)
9. Ronald, film actor who became U.S. President (6)
11. Greta, Swedish film star who retired early (5)
13. Charlton Heston's monkey business – "Planet of the . . . ." (4)
14. British actor who was an android in "Alien" (3 & 4)
15. Lavish type of film for which De Mille was known (4)
16. War film: "All Quiet on the Western . . . . ." (5)
17. Willie, country music star who was in "Barbarosa" (6)
21. Robert, star of "Ryan's Daughter" (7)
22. Rex Harrison was in "The Yellow Rolls . . . . ." (1964) (5)
23. William Powell was not 'The Fat Male' in the 30s/40s (4 & 3)

Down

2. Actor Larry Fishburne made debut in ". . . . . Now" (10)
3. Country without monarch for a now defunct film company (8)
4. "For Your Eyes . . . ." – Bond picture (4)
5. Terry Gilliam's work: ". . . . Bandits" (4)
6. Tough action-director John Woo hails from Hong . . . . (4)
9. "Robocop" is part-man, part-what? (5)
10. Jim Carrey's "Pet Detective" (3 & 7)
12. Eye-watering vegetable for Wambaugh's "The . . . . . Field" (5)
13. Nationality of writer David Mamet's "Buffalo"? (8)
18. Species of big cat roaring at start of M.G.M. features (4)
19. Sergio Leone's film: ". . . . Upon a Time in America" (4)
20. Slippery creature named "Wanda"? (4)

Across

1. Lawrence Kasdan directed the movie "The Big . . . . ." (5)
7. Queen whom Anna Neagle played in "60 Glorious Years" (8)
8. Rank of Peckinpah's "Dundee" played by Charlton Heston (5)
10. No champers for Elle, model/actress in "Sirens"? (10)
12. John, actor who starred in the movie "Broken Arrow" (8)
14. Rik Mayall as ghost-movie: "Drop Dead . . . ." (4)
16. Actor, Mr. Lithgow, starred in movie "Raising Cain" (4)
17. If the film is his first, then the director must be one (8)
20. British actor, played Dracula in Coppola's version (4 & 6)
23. Douglas Bader biopic – ". . . . . for the Sky" (5)
24. Snatches from movies shown for publicity purposes (8)
25. Roadside hotel such as place featured in movie "Psycho" (5)

Down

1. Building material for movie name: "The . . . . . . Garden" (6)
2. Actress Claire Bloom's name holds weaving machine (4)
3. Walking affliction Hoffman put on for "Midnight Cowboy" (4)
4. Metal in Jane Fonda film: ". . . . .yard Blues" (5)
5. Louis, jazz-trumpeter, appeared in movie "Paris Blues" (9)
6. Cursed, like the children in Joseph Losey's sci-fi movie (6)
9. Shaving item for Bill Murray in film: "The . . . . .'s Edge" (5)
11. Burt, wrote the score for "What's New Pussycat?" (9)
13. Film "Steel Magnolias" hides a plastic golf ball-holder (3)
15. Musical instrument – much heard on Indian film soundtracks (5)
16. ". . . . . . Edge" – Glenn Close and Jeff Bridges thriller (6)
18. Ms. Roberts, awarded a BAFTA for her role in "Yanks" (6)
19. Apology for Barbara Stanwyck film: ". . . . . Wrong Number" (5)
21. Computer info for "Star Trek: Generations" android? (4)
22. Italian actor Franco – or man who fiddled as Rome burned (4)

Across

6. ". . . . . King George" (1994) (3, 7, 2)
8. The rampagers in "Riot in Cell Block Eleven" were (7)
9. Special target audience holds area where vicar serves (5)
10. Neon sign outside cinema conceals word for ages (4)
12. Riot is altered for "Il Postino" actor, Massimo (6)
14. Sword the Cossacks rattled in the film "October" (5)
15. What you do to a movie soundtrack C.D. when you get home (6)
16. Comic film amuses the crowd – with employments inside (4)
19. Caring hospital worker completes a "Carry On" title (5)
21. Change o' client for Australian actress Diane (7)
22. Does "Butterfly Kiss"-director Michael need thermals? (12)

Down

1. Her noise changes for main female figures in films (8)
2. Bread maker – or Marilyn Monroe's real surname (5)
3. Screen gangsters conceal an anxious guilt (5)
4. "Top Hat"-star Fred; could "dance a little" (7)
5. Initial loss to "Ghost", leaving thrower of party (4)
6. Loretta Young's nursery rhyme: ". . . . . Mice"? (5 & 5)
7. Arab rain storms hide Christopher Walken movie title (10)
11. "A Fish Called Wanda" hides pale complexion (3)
12. Does "Elmer Gantry" end with an attempt? (3)
13. Another name for the condition of 6 Across? (8)
14. Between Sixth and Eighth for Sinbad's 1958 "Voyage" (7)
17. The finest Horror movies always are (5)
18. Flourish like "Limelight" actress Claire? (5)
20. Weather condition which makes people visit cinemas (4)

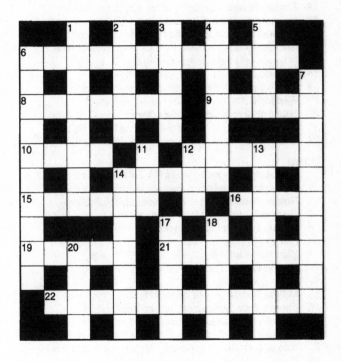

Across

3. American star who played "The Quiet Man" (4 & 5)
8. Male reversal for veteran Western actor, Jack (4)
9. Doris Day was ". . . . . Jane" (8)
10. Mailed change for "Peter's Friends" Ms. Staunton (6)
13. Reliable film actors say their lines this way (2 & 3)
14. Showbiz' arrears conceal term for Marx Bros. humour (7)
15. "The . . . and the Canary" (1939) (3)
16. Here actor hides nuclear power station (7)
17. Tones change for where studio-filming occurs (2 & 3)
21. A fictional film, without basis in fact, is this (6)
22. Biopic of Christy Brown's life – "My . . . ." (4 & 4)
23. Ms. Bancroft, U.S. star of "84 Charing Cross Road" (4)
24. Queen of Egypt famously played by Elizabeth Taylor (9)

Down

1. Film star actress who was in "A Few Good Men" (4 & 5)
2. Was confined to bed in the movie "Misery" (5 & 4)
4. Golden statuette – awarded annually (5)
5. George Formby film (1935) without restriction? (2 & 5)
6. Military Force for Sam Raimi's ". . . . of Darkness" (1992) (4)
7. Stun backwards for Streisand's 1987 film (4)
11. Singer/musician Louis, who was in "High Society" (9)
12. ". . . . . Prefer Blondes" – Marilyn Monroe movie (9)
14. Mickey Rourke/Faye Dunaway film: ". . .fly" (3)
15. Francis Ford, director of the film "Jack" (7)
18. "Star Trek" movies occur in . . . . . space (5)
19. "Dante's Inferno" gives depiction of this fiery place (4)
20. Toto jumbled for director Mr. Preminger's first name (4)

Across

1. Scorsese's unsettling 1985 black comedy of New York life (5 & 5)
8. Theresa, main actress in the film "Track 29" (7)
9. Many U.K. film actors have been to . . . . . School (5)
10. "The Magnificent Ambersons" hides an American coin (4)
11. Short term for anonymous or later in Shakespeare film (4)
12. Ms. Zetterling, Swedish director of "Scrubbers" (3)
14. Basket material for Edward Woodward's "Man" of 1973 (6)
15. In the film "Jude", the hero could be described thus (6)
18. Robert Newton's "Long John Silver" had a peg one (3)
20. The brothers Groucho, Chico, Harpo etc. (4)
21. The annual time "of Living Dangerously" (1982)? (4)
23. John, camp actor, was in "Are You Being Served?" film (5)
24. Movie actresses conceal locks of hair (7)
25. Liverpudlian actor in film – "Withnail and I" (4 & 6)

Down

1. ". . . . . . . and Old Lace"; Cary Grant 'screwball' comedy (7)
2. Title of 1950s sci-fi film about terrifying giant ants (4)
3. Peter O'Toole 1972 satire: "The . . . . . . Class" (6)
4. Timothy Hutton won Best Actor for ". . . . . People" (8)
5. Real movie stars conceal kingdom (5)
6. Rugged film star who was in "Twelve Monkeys" (5 & 6)
7. Red-haired actor who performed in "Kiss of Death" (5 & 6)
13. Airport building for film title: ". . . . . Velocity" (8)
16. So angle changed for Jackie in "The Hustler"? (7)
17. John Mills played "Scott of the Ant. . . . . ." (6)
19. Ms. Jones, actress in "Sense and Sensibility" (5)
22. Rave turnover for U.S. actress, Ms. Miles (4)

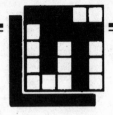

INTERMISSION

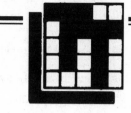

INTERMISSION

Across

1. Film of aeroplane-crash victims who resorted to cannibalism (5)
4. & 12 Across. Movie where Pacino played blind man: "The . . . ." (5 & 2, 1, 5)
10. Actor/singer Paul Robeson hides long, flowing gowns (5)
11. Feline visual organ for Stephen King-inspired film (4 & 3)
12. See 4 Across.
13. Film adaptation of Shakespeare: ". . You Like . ." (2 & 2)
15. & 26 Across. Actress from "Beetlejuice" and "Dracula" (6 & 5)
17. Ms. Fricker, "My Left Foot" Oscar-winning actress (6)
19. Art Carney film: "The . . . . Show" – not early (4)
20. Ms. Russell, who was in "Night Must Fall" (1937) (8)
23. If cowboy film is a Western, what is an oriental one? (7)
24. Raquel, stunning beauty, starred in "100 Rifles" (5)
25. Ms. Dern, was in the movie "Jurassic Park" (5)
26. See 15 Across.

Down

2. Film libraries contain a Zodiac star sign (5)
3. Judy Davis counted on films; hiding aristocratic title (8)
5. "Mary Queen of Scots" has baby beds inside (4)
6. Leslie, comic star of the "Naked Gun" series of films (7)
7. Multi-talented man, best known for "Citizen Kane" (5 & 6)
8. What type of body of sea occurs in film, "The Atlantic"? (5)
9. Polanski film: ". . . . . Maiden" (5, 3, 3)
14. Cagney sang "Give My Regards To" where? (8)
16. A-Ha! Stan changes for daughter of Vanessa Redgrave (7)
18. "The . . . . . of the Baskervilles" – Sherlock Holmes movie (5)
21. Libel over for Ginger Rogers in ".' . . . . Seeing You" (3 & 2)
22. Listen to Josef Locke in ". . . . My Song" (4)

Across

1. U.S. state, setting for 1974 movie "The Klansman" (7)
7. "Reality . . . . ." (1994) Winona Ryder film (5)
8. "Blame it on the . . . ." Dudley Moore comedy (7)
9. Steven, martial artist film star (6)
11. "The Big . . . . ." – Marx Brothers' comedy (5)
13. "Tis . . . . She's a Whore" – 1971 Italian movie (4)
14. Laurence, giant of stage and screen, was "Richard III" (7)
15. "Dead . . . ." – Nicole Kidman/Sam Neill thriller (4)
16. Is film surrealism artistic; with clever Alec inside? (5)
17. Could "Dracula" creator Bram tend furnace? (6)
21. Emilio, film actor son of Martin Sheen (7)
22. Number of Deadly Sins for Morgan Freeman-shocker (5)
23. Deny one changes for favourite female star of public (7)

Down

2. "The . . . . Wore Skirts" 1955 Tom Ewell
   comedy (10)
3. "Strictly . . . ." – Australian romance (8)
4. "The . . . .'s a Balloon" – David Niven's autobiography (4)
5. Does "Aladdin" songwriter Tim go with curry? (4)
6. Actress Candice Bergen hides Titanic-wrecking ice
   block (4)
9. Arabian chief for Valentino-film title: "The . . . . ." (5)
10. U.S. director of "Bonnie and Clyde" (1967) (6 & 4)
12. "A . . . . . Runs Through It" (1992) (5)
13. The star-studded evening of a film's first showing (8)
18. The movie where demonic Damien made entrance (4)
19. Disney/Peter Pan's "Neverneverland" holds two
    eternities (4)
20. No slow motion-filming; hiding Norwegian Capital (4)

Across

1. Rock group Queen did music for the film ". . . . Gordon" (5)
7. Eastwood played wounded Civil War man in "The . . . ." (8)
8. Golden role in movie conceals to sign on (5)
10. Budd Schulberg wrote novel/film: "On the . . . ." (10)
12. Sheath where a movie adventurer keeps his sword (8)
14. Roseanne, comic actress who took lead in "She-Devil" (4)
16. Mika reversed for "Topkapi" actor, Mr. Tamiroff (4)
17. Take 'H' and 'I' from title "Pastor Hall" for rural quality (8)
20. Horrific Cambodian-based film: ". . . . . Fields" (3 & 7)
23. Robert, star of the original "The Thirty-Nine Steps" (5)
24. With Gilbert, wrote "The Mikado" which has been filmed (8)
25. Short form of Edward for Mr. Bracken, film comic (5)

Down

1. Open pastures for the film comic, W.C.? (6)
2. Type of film which might bore viewer – not fast (4)
3. "The Way We . . . ." – Redford/Streisand love story (4)
4. Polishes – like name for most avid of film enthusiasts (5)
5. Egyptian queen once played by Hedy Lamarr (9)
6. Technical person responsible for final form of a film (6)
9. Jonathan Demme directed "The Silence of the . . . . ." (5)
11. Fair Nell I changed for film about adult male soprano (9)
13. Irish actor Stephen – star of the film "The Crying Game" (3)
15. Don't sit for River Phoenix film: ". . . . . by Me" (5)
16. What was Picasso whom Anthony Hopkins has played? (6)
18. Small, like the musical: ". . . . . . Shop of Horrors" (6)
19. Vocal imitator – many an actor is a good one (5)
21. No fat on "Ryan's Daughter" director, David? (4)
22. Precious metal for Roger Moore/Susannah York film? (4)

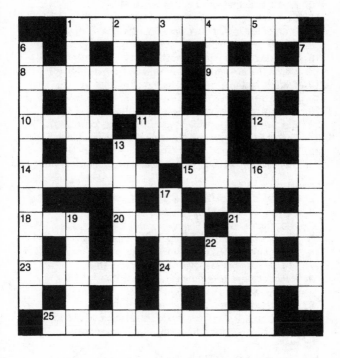

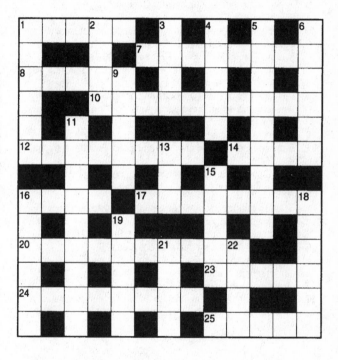

Across

6. Join me in bed for Yves Montand/Marilyn Monroe comedy? (4, 4, 4)
8. Type of sportsmen shown in cult movie "Big Wednesday" (7)
9. Interpol karate, caught on film, hides a lively dance (5)
10. Look for Madonna movie: "Desperately ....ing Susan" (4)
12. Seashore stone – wouldn't be out of place in "Beaches" (6)
14. "Un ..... en Hiver"/ "A Heart in Winter" (1991) (5)
15. Director's cap I stole on location concealed handgun (6)
16. Resounding noise for Michael Apted's "The Triple ...." (4)
19. Mr. Lorre reversal shows Mr. Flynn's beginning (5)
21. Between September and November for Eisentein's film? (7)
22. Wes Craven Horror film – not an old day-dream! (3 & 9)

Down

1. Startles changed for old term for Hollywood hopefuls (8)
2. "The Magnificent Ambersons" hides a traffic light colour (5)
3. One peck? ". .... Before Dying" (1956) & (1991) (1 & 4)
4. Paul Hogan children's film about a seal (7)
5. Writer/director Sam Raimi's "The . . . . Dead" (4)
6. Christ's final meal for Stacy Title's debut film (4 & 6)
7. Outdoor sporting venue where "The Killing" was set (10)
11. "The Color Purple" has an abbreviated Colonel within (3)
12. The movie "Crime and Punishment" hides a play on words (3)
13. Film of early Hamburg days of 'The Beatles' (8)
14. Actress Joan, hit saucy fame in films like "The Bitch" (7)
17. Hard men like the "Guys" Lancaster and Douglas played (5)
18. Sean Penn/Gary Oldman film: ". . . . . of Grace" (5)
20. Genuine-sounding spool on which cinematic film rotates (4)

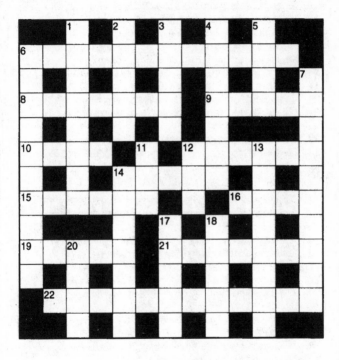

Across

3. Gillian, "High Tide" director, sounds mighty-limbed (9)
8. "Never Give a Sucker an . . . . Break" (1941) (4)
9. Singer/actress Madonna's film: "Body of . . . ." (8)
10. Individual pictures on roll of film (6)
13. Chambers complete movie title: "Four . . . . ." (5)
14. Rupert Everett starred in ". . . . . . . Country" (1984) (7)
15. Mr. Lee, director of "Eat Drink Man Woman" (3)
16. Fly without landing; hiding Sean Connery sci-fi film (7)
17. Potato snack for "Lassie Come Home" actor, Donald? (5)
21. Does a cut "Eraserhead" hold something sharper? (6)
22. Louise, played harsh nurse in "One Flew over the Cuckoo's Nest" (8)
23. Mr/Ms. Davidson who appeared in "The Crying Game" (4)
24. French film: ". . . . . Strangest Way" (1994) (4, 2, 3)

Down

1. U.S. President in film: ". . . . . in Paris" (9)
2. Singer/actor Harry, who appeared in "Kansas City" (9)
4. Producer frees extra money – with tough actor Tom inside (5)
5. Wartime spy/love story: ". . . . . . . Through" (1992) (7)
6. Anti-marijuana film of 1936: ". . . .er Madness" (4)
7. English jail for "Farewell to the King" Mr. Nolte? (4)
11. Festive holiday at centre of "It's a Wonderful Life" (9)
12. Alan Rudolph film: ". . . . . and the Vicious Circle" (3 & 6)
14. "Butch Cassidy . . . the Sundance Kid" (3)
15. Famous thriller: ". . . . . There Were None" (3 & 4)
18. . . . . . Vader, sinister figure from "Star Wars" (5)
19. Cecil B. de Mille epic: ". . . .patra" (4)
20. 'The Beatles' 1970 documentary film: "Let . . . ." (2 & 2)

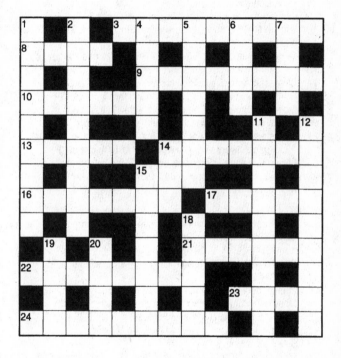

Across

1. Film where Tommy Lee Jones took over a battleship (5 & 5)
8. Bob, London actor, came up against "Roger Rabbit" (7)
9. The aroma "of Fear" for "Naked Gun 2½"? (5)
10. Where DeNiro terrorised Jessica Lange and family – "Cape . . . ." (4)
11. Winged creature for Eastwood film on Charlie Parker (4)
12. Mr. Kline, Mr. Costner, short version of first name (3)
14. Cyclops-trait for Brando's film: ". . . . . . .d Jacks" (3 & 3)
15. Hoffman and Streep's 1979 battling family name (6)
18. Does "Thelma and Louise" hold a tree? (3)
20. Visual organs for film – "The . . . . of Laura Mars" (4)
21. Tiny stones which were "True" for John Wayne in 1969 (4)
23. A cut-price cinema ticket is an . . . . . hard to refuse (5)
24. Movie actress Eileen, who was in "Private Benjamin" (7)
25. ". . . . . are Easy" – Jeff Goldblum-as-an-alien movie (5 & 5)

Down

1. Minor actors sometimes do this to a star in a movie (7)
2. Daily film rushes hide Eire's Lower Parliamentary house (4)
3. Filmed John LeCarré novel: "The . . . . . . House" (1990) (6)
4. Ones who know how film world works – not outsiders (8)
5. Nationality of Anthony Quinn's Zorba (5)
6. & 13 Down. Pedro Almodovar 1996 film (3, 6, 2 & 2, 6)
7. U.S. director of the biopic of Richard "Nixon" (6 & 5)
13. See 6 Down.
16. Rick, who played Barney Rubble in "The Flintstones" (7)
17. Dubbed "Bugsy" film conceals a night-biter (6)
19. U.S. crime syndicate shown in "The Godfather" films (5)
22. The animal hunted in title of Seventies Vietnam picture (4)

Across

1. Shore-breaking item; passion-metaphor in old films (1 & 4)
4. Mr. Martin, who was in film "Dirty Rotten Scoundrels" (5)
10. An aid changed for American actor, Mr. Quinn (5)
11. Comes back – like Val Kilmer's "Batman"? (7)
12. Lack of exit for Costner/Hackman 1987 thriller? (2, 3, 3)
13. Currency paid at box office by Italian cinema-goers (4)
15. Michael Caine gangland movie: "Get . . . . . ." (1971) (6)
17. Derek, T.V.'s 'Claudius', was in "The Odessa File" (6)
19. Without clothing for the 1980 movie – "The . . . .
    Bomb"? (4)
20. Method of giving hair body used by movie stylists (8)
23. Singer/dancer Donald, played Buster Keaton in 1957 (7)
24. Comic Eric Idle reacts; concealing a lazy individual (5)
25. Mr. Murphy, comic star of "The Nutty Professor" (5)
26. The cartoon mouse forever chased by Tom the cat (5)

Down

2. Bereaved wife for Chevalier's film, "The Merry . . . . ." (5)
3. Played sweep in "Mary Poppins" (surname
   and initial) (7 & 1)
5. The film title "State Fair" hides a London art gallery (4)
6. "Acrophobia" for James Stewart movie? (7)
7. The director of the movie "Judge Dredd" (5 & 6)
8. Psychoanalysis-founder whom Montgomery Clift
   played (5)
9. Kristofferson/Streisand movie (1976) (1, 4, 2, 4)
14. In slapstick, it was common to fall on this part of body (8)
16. Robert, lead actor in the movie "Up Close and
    Personal" (7)
18. Egyptian capital for name of George Sanders' film (5)
21. Potboiler of a movie contains one who lubricates (5)
22. Giant idol of cinema contains opposing position (4)

Across
1. Gloria, played Norma Desmond in "Sunset Boulevard" (7)
7. Alain, French star of "Borsalino" (1970) (5)
8. Robert, tough star of the original "Cape Fear" (1962) (7)
9. Title of Gena Rowlands (1980) film (6)
11. Hide von Stroheim's work and conceal English county (5)
13. "The Lion . . . ." – Disney cartoon (4)
14. Move forward like money given upfront to scriptwriter (7)
15. Writer Kurt Vonnegut's filmed work contains courage (4)
16. "A Touch of . . . . ." (1973) British farce (5)
17. "Passenger 57" star, Mr. Snipes (6)
21. Mobile home for: ". . . . . . . to Vaccares" (1974) (7)
22. Undressed for David Cronenberg film: ". . . . . Lunch" (5)
23. Bank teller, told to "Stick 'em up" in gangster movies (7)

Down
2. The Presidential home struck in "Independence Day" (5 & 5)
3. Actor Derek Bond played ". . . . . Nickleby" (8)
4. Does a star's salary bonus contain her burden? (4)
5. Watch actor Dean Stockwell to find a place of water (4)
6. Without money – or description of a bad quality film (4)
9. Ms. Close: Cruella de Vil in live action "101 Dalmatians" (5)
10. Dennis Quaid fantasy of miniaturised voyage inside body (10)
12. Tusk matter for James, director of Indian-based films (5)
13. U.K. director of film drama "Raining Stones" (3 & 5)
18. "The King and I" concerns the King of where? (4)
19. "East of" Paradise for James Dean movie? (4)
20. A rat returned for the "Gone with the Wind" homestead (4)

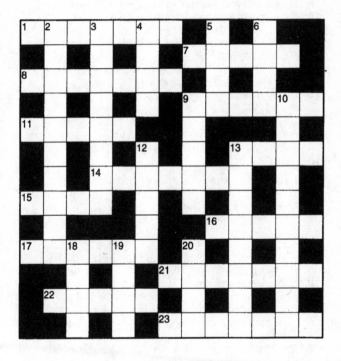

Across

1. Saucy cartoon girl of 1920s–1930s, ". . . . . Boop" (5)
7. Eat up this green for late Bond-movie producer, Cubby (8)
8. Ms. Garson who 'married' in "Goodbye Mr. Chips" (5)
10. Eating-place for Arthur Penn film: "Alice's
. . . ." (10)
12. Director needles star; containing something unnecessary (8)
14. A corner for Errol Flynn film: ". . . . of Darkness"? (4)
16. Almost chokes or name for jokes in comedy films (4)
17. Charlotte, starred in "The Night Porter" (8)
20. Coloured facial hair for Disney's: ". . . . .'s
Ghost" (10)
23. Striped cat for Woody Allen's "What's Up, ... Lily?" (5)
24. A thrilling action movie certainly can be (8)
25. Sergio, director of films such as "A Fistful of Dollars" (5)

Down

1. Large Male for Neeson-as-prizefighter movie:
"The . . . ." (3 & 3)
2. Cinema row sounds like trickle from eye (4)
3. Show Rita Hayworth's concealment of legal summons (4)
4. Baden Powell-disciple for movie – "The Last Boy
. . . . ." (5)
5. Sad film depiction of T. S. Eliot's first marriage (3, 3, 3)
6. Custer's battle giving movie title – ". . . . . . Big Horn" (6)
9. Gaelic dances for spools of celluloid? (5)
11. "Die Hard with a . . . ." for third in the series (9)
13. Does "Spartacus" contain a healthy resort? (3)
15. Physical activity completes movie – "This . . . . .ing
Life" (5)
16. Ornate drinking vessel seen in banquet-set films (6)
18. English dragon-slaying saint for actor, Mr. Clooney? (6)
19. Takes over for roller-item used in film "Xanadu" (5)
21. Jerome Kern earned a lot; yet hid a sea eagle (4)
22. U.S. coin in documentary: "Brother Can You Spare a
. . . .?" (4)

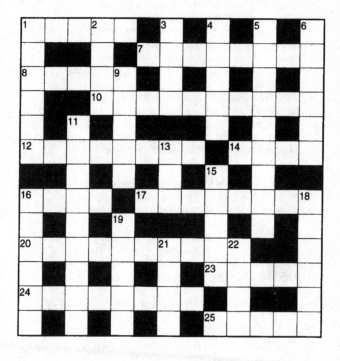

Across

6. Film-maker's version of work; unhindered by studio (9 & 3)
8. One thought guilty of crime – Boulting Brothers film (7)
9. Cop's intuition for Laughton's back in "Notre Dame"? (5)
10. It leaves "Lolita" for another woman's name (4)
12. "Me and My Gal" is on screen, concealing girl's name (6)
14. Some people have been known to, in a hot airless cinema (5)
15. Sad emotion for Bob Hope film: ". . . . . . ful Jones" (1949) (6)
16. Say "I'm a Movie Mogul" – to hide a Mosque prayer-leader (4)
19. After nipping out, once more took your cinema seat (2–3)
21. Kirk's rank on T.V. before Admiral in Star Trek movies (7)
22. Very independent director of "The Player" (6 & 6)

Down

1. What was Hulk Hogan before he entered films? (8)
2. Within a film's crew is hidden a wall-drilling item (5)
3. Tennessee Williams filmed play: "Sweet Bird of . . . . ." (5)
4. Road-surfacing material for film: "The . . . . Jungle" (7)
5. Set alight for alternative title of Brando's "Queimada!" (4)
6. Film of Michael Crichton novel on sex in the workplace (10)
7. Movie in which Travolta plays a man with psychic powers (10)
11. British comedy: "The Wrong Arm of the . . ." (1962) (3)
12. Cole Porter musical-film: ". . .thing Goes" (3)
13. Writer/director of "The Evil Dead" Horror films (3 & 5)
14. Decade when most W.W.II movies are set (7)
17. Ridley and Tony, British directors/brothers (5)
18. Fruit for Disney's "The . . . . . Dumpling Gang" (5)
20. ". . . .! Or My Mum Will Shoot" – Stallone comedy (4)

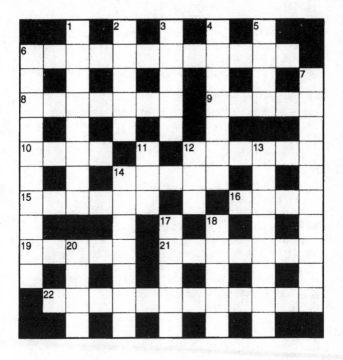

Across

3. One of the principal actresses in "The Crucible" (4 & 5)
8. Lex Luthor is this kind of enemy to Superman (4)
9. "The . . . . Horseman" (1979) (8)
10. Slayer completes 1975 film: "The . . . . . . Elite" (6)
13. Pay a call on "The" name of a 1964 Ingrid Bergman film (5)
14. Luis Buñuel and Salvador Dali made this style of film (7)
15. Frank Sinatra musical: ". . . Joey" (3)
16. & 24 Across. George & Quentin, "From Dusk Till Dawn" stars (7 & 9)
17. Nuclear plant thriller: "The . . . . . Syndrome" (5)
21. Lone Western character featured in several films (6)
22. U.S. slang for soft shoes and name of Redford movie (8)
23. Tim Burton's star-studded flick: ". . . . Attacks" (4)
24. See 16 Across.

Down

1. John, bald U.S. actor, appeared in "Dangerous Liaisons" (9)
2. English actor Christopher who was in "Shallow Grave" (9)
4. The Marx Brothers spent "A Night at the . . . . ." (5)
5. Max von Sydow Horror film: ". . . . . . . Things" (7)
6. The film "Klute" may conceal a stringed instrument (4)
7. Terry Jones film: ". . . . the Viking" (4)
11. Ernest, U.S. writer depicted "In Love and War" (9)
12. 3 golf strokes under par for French film: "L' . . . ." (9)
14. Al Jolson film: ". . . It With Songs" (3)
15. Flawless; as in Jamie Lee Curtis 1985 movie title (7)
18. Does screen actress Greer Garson hide a burning crime? (5)
19. Greta Garbo played ". . . . Karenina" (4)
20. "Krakatoa, East of . . . ." (1968) (4)

Across

1. Deliverance from sin as in "The Shawshank
   . . . ." (10)
8. Illegal drug going with filmic "Agony" of Michelangelo (7)
9. ". . . . . People's Money" – Danny DeVito comedy (5)
10. Cinema confectionery – Choc' . . . . (4)
11. Leather lash wielded well by Ms. Pfeiffer as
    Catwoman (4)
12. Verbal contract contains what film stars are paid to do (3)
14. Films were – in the days before the advent of sound (6)
15. Robin Williams was in "The World According
    . . . . . ." (2 & 4)
18. ". . . About Eve" (1950) Bette Davis film (3)
20. "Last . . . . to Brooklyn" – starred Jennifer Jason Leigh (4)
21. Hippy musical film with "The Age of Aquarius" song in it (4)
23. "The Distinguished Gentleman", Mr. Murphy (5)
24. From Burma for 1956 film: "The . . . . Harp" (7)
25. One of the Musketeers for title: ". . . . .' .
    Daughter" (10)

Down

1. Ken, provocative director of "Altered States" (7)
2. ". . . . M for Murder" – Hitchcock movie (4)
3. ". . . . . . Force be with you" – "Star Wars" slogan (3 & 3)
4. Emma, won Oscar for "In the Name of the Father" role (8)
5. Tessie, large music-hall singer, was in "The Shiralee" (5)
6. Actor who played creepy psychopath in "Seven" (5 & 6)
7. Robert Altman film; French for ready-to-wear (4, 1, 6)
13. Improper – as in Redford's "Proposal" to Demi Moore (8)
16. Dramatic film centred around Mozart's life (7)
17. "Pack up your troubles in your old" what in W.W.I
    films? (6)
19. Daily change for Groucho Marx's "tattooed lady" (5)
22. Maria Callas's first name holds operatic song inside (4)

Across

1. What kind of creature is cartoon 'Mickey'? (5)
4. Disney's dog with planetary associations? (5)
10. "Charlie Chan at the . . . . ." (1936) (5)
11. Judy Davis was in the movie: "A . . . . to India" (7)
12. Name of ocean in Louis Malle's ". . . . . . . City" (1981) (8)
13. Film: "The VIPs" partly reversed for black marketeer (4)
15. Robert, played an obsessive follower in "The Fan" (6)
17. Do ring changes for Charles, the dad in "Beethoven" (6)
19. Silence which usually falls once a film starts (4)
20. Glen, country singer, appeared in "True Grit" (8)
23. Ms. Young, starred in "A Night to Remember" (1942) (7)
24. Take 'd', 'r' and 'p' from 14 Down for atmospheric layer (5)
25. Errol, star of films such as "Gentleman Jim" (5)
26. James Dean's was "Without a Cause" (5)

Down

2. Child star Tatum who was in "The Bad News Bears" (5)
3. 1980 David Cronenberg Horror movie (8)
5. "Raiders of the . . . . Ark" (1981) (4)
6. Caught, as in Nicolas Cage film: ". . . . . . . in Paradise" (7)
7. Burt Reynolds' 150% Policeman? (3, 3, 1, 4)
8. Month of Doris Day movie: ". . . . . in Paris" (5)
9. Gaunt-faced villain in many Spaghetti Westerns (3, 3, 5)
14. 1994 Movie about skydiving criminals (4 & 4)
16. Part of nose King Kong flared when angry (7)
18. Country where the Manga cartoons originated (5)
21. Run off to get married as Ollie and love do in "Our Wife" (5)
22. "Nuts" reversed for what publicity says a film may do (4)

Across

1. "Henry: Portrait of . . . . Killer" (1990) (1 & 6)
7. On rental for Peter Fonda's Western: "The . . . . . Hand" (5)
8. Ms. Hershey, actress in "The Last Temptation of Christ" (7)
9. "The . . . . . . of the Beehive" (1973) (6)
11. Outspoken U.S. comic Mr. Bruce, shown in Bob Fosse film (5)
13. "Intruder in the . . . ." (1949) (4)
14. Stanley Kubrick directed "2001: A Space . . . ." (7)
15. James, actor who starred in "Rollerball" (4)
16. Michael, London actor, in the movie "California Suite" (5)
17. Area where Janet Leigh met her watery end in "Psycho" (6)
21. Papal home seen in film "Never Take No for an Answer" (7)
22. Not true, like Curtis's nose in "The Boston Strangler" (5)
23. ". . . Big . . . ." – Dennis Quaid (1986) movie (3 & 4)

Down

2. Travelling-wagon for title of John Wayne movie (10)
3. Anne Bancroft played Mrs. . . . . in "The Graduate" (8)
4. Actress Laura Dern's name contains a distinctive air (4)
5. Slang for Harvey Keitel's job in "Taxi Driver" (4)
6. Scared emotion for title of Mark Wahlberg film (1996) (4)
9. Errol Flynn, Douglas Fairbanks Snr. were . . . . .bucklers (5)
10. Those unable to sleep who turn to late night films on T.V. (10)
12. How jet-setting film superstars travel (2 & 3)
13. Explosive stick for comic movie: ". . . . . . . Chicken" (8)
18. No ban on film conceals place in Scotland (4)
19. Uncomplicated Chaplin movie title: ". . . . Street"? (4)
20. Use soap and water for film – "Angels . . . . Their Faces" (4)

Across

1. Phil Silvers was this Sgt. on TV; Steve Martin on film (5)
7. Joan, Faye Dunaway played her in "Mommie Dearest" (8)
8. Does Kurt Russell's name conceal a surgical support? (5)
10. The one who specializes for Stallone/Stone movie (10)
12. Change 'nine mill.' for Vincente, the M.G.M. musical man (8)
14. Hairless state of film actor Telly Savalas (4)
16. Simple – like Dennis Hopper and Peter Fonda's "Rider"? (4)
17. Meaty Demi Moore comedy: "The . . . . '. Wife"? (8)
20. Principal actor in Altman's "The Player" (3 & 7)
23. In cop movie car chases, the red warning device heard (5)
24. Alfred Hitchcock's ornithological nightmare film (3 & 5)
25. Peter Greenaway's "The . . . . . of an Architect" (1987) (5)

Down

1. Not top for film: "Voyage to the . . . . . . of the Sea" (6)
2. "The Taming of the Shrew" as a musical: ". . . . Me Kate" (4)
3. Rice changed for Julia Roberts' actor brother (4)
4. Expletives; type of words that occur too often in films (5)
5. Among the ones put forward for Academy Award (9)
6. Before a film can be released, it needs to be . . . . . . (6)
9. Sandra Bullock thriller set aboard a bomb-carrying bus (5)
11. Single season for title: "It Happened . . . ." (3 & 6)
13. Film comics: Bud Abbott and . . . Costello (3)
15. Coins changed for movie megastars (5)
16. Property and money left when wealthy actor dies (6)
18. Forename of director, Mr. Pollack (6)
19. "Frankenstein"-actor, Mr. Karloff (5)
21. 1973 Peter Sellers comedy: "Soft . . . . ., Hard Battles" (4)
22. Leonard Bernstein's musical: "West . . . . Story" (4)

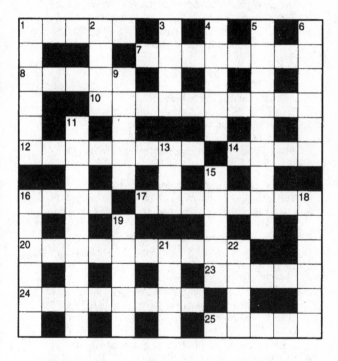

Across

6. Hitchcock-loving director of "Mission: Impossible" (5 & 7)
8. Regrets in a movie story – hiding Greek white wine (7)
9. Dance which for 6 Down was "Last . . . . . in Paris" (5)
10. Peter Fonda film: ". . . . Season". Not closed (4)
12. Jack, tragic/comic actor, sounds like a citrus fruit (6)
14. More wisdom for Claudette Colbert's "The . . . . .
    Sex"? (5)
15. Not spotted by eye for Joel McCrea-film, "The
    . . . . . ."? (6)
16. Anthony Quinn's name hides slang for 1 of 5 children (4)
19. "The . . . . ." – movie about a coven of juvenile witches (5)
21. Arena for play completes movie title: ". . . . . . . of
    Blood" (7)
22. Streep/Bacon movie about white-water rafting (3, 5, 4)

Down

1. Unfaithful husband's lover for title of 1992 movie (8)
2. The film "Frantic" contains a high-spirited caper (5)
3. Lundgren's masculine hero in "Masters of the
   Universe" (2-3)
4. This cat in the Clouseau movie titles was "Pink" (7)
5. Remove Lucky from "O Lucky Man" for Arabian place (4)
6. Bernardo, director of the film "Stealing Beauty" (10)
7. "Get Shorty" director, Barry (10)
11. Metal of Richard Dreyfuss and Danny DeVito's "Men" (3)
12. Lion in Zodiac for director of the past, Mr. McCarey (3)
13. "The Englishman Who Went Up A Hill But Came
    Down A . . . ." (8)
14. Genre of movie for which John Ford was famous (7)
17. Mr. McQueen, who starred in the movie "Papillon" (5)
18. Conrad's ". . . . . of Darkness" inspired "Apocalypse
    Now" (5)
20. A Cherokee-centred movie conceals a nagging pain (4)

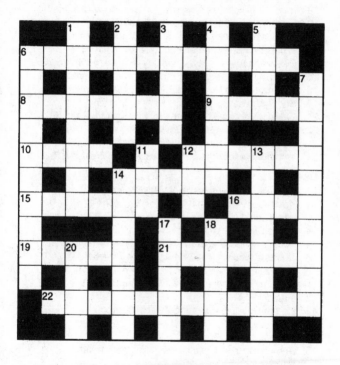

Across

3. & 17 Across. Film: ". . . . . Versus . . . . .
   Flynt" (3, 6 & 5)
8. "I am okay with this video but I'm running wild inside" (4)
9. Film by makers of "Trainspotting" – set in Swansea (4 & 4)
10. "Bitter Moon" actor Peter has a wolflike wild dog's name (6)
13. What you'll surely do at a good comedy film (5)
14. Playwright Steven played bad guy in "Beverly Hills Cop" (7)
15. Films of urban decay can hide fine hair of animal (3)
16. "Women on the Verge of a . . . . Breakdown" (1988) (7)
17. See 3 Across.
21. When a star's hairline starts to, he might try a wig (6)
22. Human killing for title of David Mamet's 1991 film (8)
23. Ken Russell's "The . . . . of the White Worm" (4)
24. Immature pistols for Lou Diamond Phillips Western? (5 & 4)

Down

1. Spanish city gives name of Whit Stillman movie (9)
2. Kevin Costner/Whitney Houston film: "The
   . . . ." (9)
4. Film adaptation of Arthur Hailey book (5)
5. Sidney, handcuffed to Tony Curtis in "The Defiant Ones" (7)
6. Suitable food for Roy Rogers' horse Trigger? (4)
7. Jeff Fahey starred in "The . . . .mower Man" (4)
11. Tom, actor helping Finney into costumes in "The
    Dresser" (9)
12. Illeana Douglas was songwriter in "Grace
    . . . ." (2, 2, 5)
14. Public transport for Monroe in ". . . Stop"? (3)
15. Something it seems the British film industry always
    needs (7)
18. "How . . . . . Was My Valley" (1941) (5)
19. Harrison Ford played Han . . . . in "Star Wars" (4)
20. O'Toole/Hepburn film: "The . . . . in Winter" (4)

Across

1. Demi Moore/Michael Douglas – sexual harassment film (10)
8. & 15 Across. Ken Russell film on changing consciousness (7 & 6)
9. "Just a spoonful of . . . . ." in "Mary Poppins" song (5)
10. Actress Louise Fletcher's surname has to engrave inside (4)
11. Alexander Hall film: ". . . . Comes Mr. Jordan" (4)
12. Are changes needed for Irish actor, Stephen? (3)
14. Film company behind the ingenious picture "Toy Story" (6)
15. See 8 Across.
18. Inside Batman's cowl lurks another night creature (3)
20. Stephen King film: ". . . .ful Things" (4)
21. Bruce, played spineless Sheriff in "Last Man Standing" (4)
23. Central cinema walkway dividing the rows (5)
24. Pronounce sin-free – as may happen in movie "Absolution" (7)
25. Gallic oral intimacy for film title? (6 & 4)

Down

1. Presumably, what a movie detective does (7)
2. Fantasy 'Shangri-La' was a sight for these kind of eyes (4)
3. Tim Robbins' climbing frame: "Jacob's . . . . . ." (6)
4. Movie title: "The Usual . . . ." (8)
5. Connery's successor as James Bond, ... Moore (5)
6. Actor who played Scotty in "Star Trek" films (5 & 6)
7. Director of 4 Down has a melodious-sounding name (5 & 6)
13. British actor in the movie "When Saturday Comes" (4 & 4)
16. He wilts – altered – for "Dragonheart" actor David (7)
17. Tip out her ash for film borrowing ideas from another (6)
19. Not a winner for film title: ". . . . . Takes All" (5)
22. Film song "As Time Goes By" contains this Italian wine (4)

44

Across

1. U.K. Policeman – or name Scorsese uses with DeNiro (5)
4. "Beau Geste" camel base hides peachy ice-cream dessert (5)
10. "My Own Private . . . . .", River Phoenix movie (5)
11. Some cop changes for what movie music writers do (7)
12. Samuel, hitman with Travolta in "Pulp Fiction" (1 & 7)
13. Naval hailing term for Eleanor Powell film: "Ship . . . ." (4)
15. Belonging to Stallone's boxing character? (6)
17. Indigenous New Zealanders, seen in "Once Were Warriors" (6)
19. A thrill – or blow you might see – in martial arts movie (4)
20. The highest accolade at the Cannes Film Festival (5 & 3)
23. Early part of day for Julie Delpy film: "Before . . . ." (7)
24. Pointed name for Mr. Milligan who was in "The Magic Christian" (5)
25. Warts reversed for "Wizard of Oz" Scarecrow's filling (5)
26. Creature with hypnotic eyes in the cartoon "Jungle Book" (5)

Down

2. Maureen, fiery actress in the movie "The Quiet Man" (5)
3. Part of New York Eddie Murphy's "Vampire" came from (8)
5. Ms. Thompson, actress once married to Kenneth Branagh (4)
6. Relationship Keith bears to David Carradine (7)
7. Oral contact by murderer for early Kubrick film? (7 & 4)
8. Occupation Christian Slater would cite on his passport? (5)
9. She played "The French Lieutenant's Woman" (5 & 6)
14. Italian cheese sprinkled over food in Mafia movies (8)
16. Hard-shelled fruit often seen in desert island-set films (7)
18. By today's standards, many old films do seem . . . . . (5)
21. What would you do with lemonade at a cinema? (5)
22. A gin changes for Italian beauty, Ms. Lollobrigida (4)

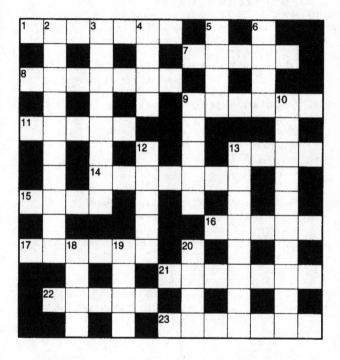

Across

1. Hopefully, what an assistant does for the director (5)
7. "Even . . . . Get the Blues" (1993) (8)
8. Shape of the table in King Arthur-based films (5)
10. Krzysztof, director of the "Three Colours" trilogy (10)
12. Alec, star of "The Lavender Hill Mob" (8)
14. Death for me in Cagney movie – "Each Dawn . . . ."? (1 & 3)
16. Leap around for Clint Eastwood's ashen-faced "Rider" (4)
17. Novelist, 'D. H.', whose "Sons and Lovers" has been filmed (8)
20. A blind liar changes for "The Exorcist" actress (5 & 5)
23. Nude film of Mike Leigh? (5)
24. Boom-holder or person rung when you need phone number (8)
25. You may shed them while watching a sentimental movie (5)

Down

1. German director of "Fitzcarraldo", Werner (6)
2. Colour in John Hughes' film – "Pretty in . . . ." (4)
3. Sausages in buns at cinema – "Hot . . . ." (4)
4. Nicholson/Cruise military movie ". Few . . . . Men" (1 & 4)
5. United States leader in film – "The American . . . ." (9)
6. Change praise for what ambitious new actors do (6)
9. . . . . . Dors, actress who was in the 1948 "Oliver Twist" (5)
11. Infamous U.S. gangster played by Warren Oates (9)
13. Al Pacino/Ellen Barkin thriller: ". . . of Love" (3)
15. Jon Voight's locomotive in title: "The Runaway . . . . ." (5)
16. Soft headrest in bed for Day/Hudson's ". . . . . . Talk" (6)
18. Moses leaving Israel gives you name of Preminger film (6)
19. "Heavenly Creatures" actress, Ms. Peirse (5)
21. Film with a speaking baby: ". . . . Who's Talking" (4)
22. Gear change for movie – "A . . . . in Harlem" (4)

Across

1. Gotham City is . . . . . .'. home (7)
7. You could have "Apollo 13" Kevin for breakfast (5)
8. Nail kit for way Neeson was dressed in "Rob Roy"? (2, 1, 4)
9. Buster, shellfish-sounding "Flash Gordon" star (6)
11. Liza Minnelli played . . . . . Bowles in "Cabaret" (5)
13. "Barefoot in the . . . ." (1967) Redford/Fonda comedy (4)
14. Fear of heights for Hitchcock's 1958 movie? (7)
15. Hidden footwear in quirky film "Gumshoe"? (4)
16. "When . . . . . Met Sally" (1989) Love story (5)
17. Mel, director of "Blazing Saddles" (6)
21. Rosalind, actress who starred in "His Girl Friday" (7)
22. John Boorman film of 1987 – "Hope and . . . . ." (5)
23. Naval rank of Nelson, as played by Peter Finch (7)

Down

2. She was wife of Michael Douglas in "Fatal Attraction" (4 & 6)
3. Slogan in Hippy era films: ". . . . ., not War!" (4 & 4)
4. Jodie Foster's wilderness character (1994) (4)
5. Look into affair to complete "Sabrina" (1954)'s title (4)
6. Ty, baseball legend, played in biopic by Tommy Lee Jones (4)
9. Sean Penn's brother, acted in "Mulholland Falls" (5)
10. Sixties sci-fi beauty played by Jane Fonda (10)
12. Obnoxious kids for Laurel and Hardy film title (5)
13. Roman, Polish director of "Chinatown" (8)
18. "You . . . . Live Twice" (1967) (4)
19. Mr. Russell, who played the main role in "Escape to L.A." (4)
20. Terence Stamp movie: "Billy . . . ." (1962) (4)

Across

6. 'Blondie' singer, was in the creepy "Videodrome" (7 & 5)
8. Set Ivan around for most conceited of film actors (7)
9. Noise made to block out swearing in movies (5)
10. Why should Rip Torn conceal intravenous device? (4)
12. One of the animal characters in "Wind in the Willows" (6)
14. Richard Burton movie: "Look Back in . . . . ." (5)
15. It's best to . . . . . . the views of certain film critics (6)
16. Mass of ice in Steven Spielberg's name (4)
19. The rebel "Bowery Boys" have concealed joint in arm (5)
21. Give Paulette Goddard credit; containing shoulder-piece (7)
22. Mike Newell directed: ". . . . . and a Funeral" (4 & 8)

Down

1. Boil vino changed for film title: "Living in . . . ." (8)
2. Colour in Gerard Depardieu movie: ". . . . . Card" (5)
3. ". . . . . Men Can't Jump" (1992) (5)
4. One who bets for James Caan film title: "The . . . ." (7)
5. Children's whale movie: ". . . . Willy" (4)
6. British actor, star of Bond-spoof "Casino Royale" (5 & 5)
7. Fruit and field entrances for film: "Meet the . . . ." (10)
11. Carl Franklin directed the film ". . . False Move" (3)
12. Dampened – like Esther Williams in "Dangerous When . . ." (3)
13. Taking without permission, like Bertolucci's "Beauty" (8)
14. Type of design graphic artist on film is involved in (7)
17. John Travolta's "Saturday Night" virus? (5)
18. U.S. sweet-product for 1968 satirical movie (5)
20. Breathe air out for David Hemmings' film: ". . . . Up" (4)

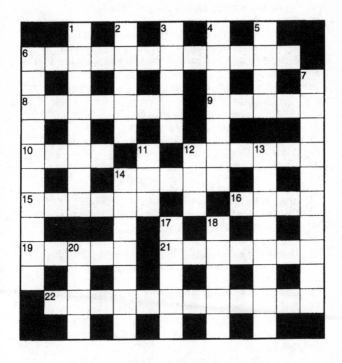

48

Across

3. Living on after Anthony Hopkins movie of Picasso? (9)
8. "Robin . . . . : Men in Tights" (1993) (4)
9. Heavy pornography for Paul Schrader's 1978 film name (8)
10. State of the central figure in "The Diary of a Madman"? (6)
13. Type of fish fills title of film: "Paris . . . . ." (1991) (5)
14. Another term for hairdresser who works on cast's looks (7)
15. Speak; as in film ". . . It with Flowers (A Human Story)" (3)
16. Jodie Foster won an Oscar for her role in "The . . . ." (7)
17. "The . . . . . Has Landed" (1976) (5)
21. Devourers – such as "Zombie Flesh . . . . . ." (6)
22. Lucid ire changed for derisive French film title (8)
23. Actor Mr. Arkin, starred in "Catch 22" (4)
24. He played Jim Morrison in the movie "The Doors" (3 & 6)

Down

1. Is the actor Mr. Slater a follower of Jesus? (9)
2. Child's pavement game identifies Walter Matthau film (9)
4. Much-filmed Poe story: "The Fall of the House of . . . . ." (5)
5. U.S. film publication; it's "the spice of life" (7)
6. Police squad to which Elliott Gould belongs in "Busting" (4)
7. Slang term for a police informer in crime films (4)
11. Anthony, director of "The English Patient" (9)
12. Barbra, star of "The Mirror Has Two Faces" (9)
14. Does the film "Sadie McKee" conceal a mournful quality? (3)
15. "Jonathan Livingston . . . ." (1973) (7)
18. "The Wild . . . . ." starred Burton, Harris and Moore (5)
19. Long live – ". . . . Zapata" (1952) (4)
20. Cary Grant film: "That Touch of . . . ." (4)

Across

1. Chazz, writer/actor of "A Bronx Tale" (10)
8. Director Michael Curtiz's Eastern European country (7)
9. "They . . . . . be Giants" – George C. Scott film (1972) (5)
10. Does Robert Mitchum conceal a pal in his name? (4)
11. Beefy baseball part for Kevin Costner: ". . . . Durham"? (4)
12. Doris Day's hot beverage: ". . . for Two" (3)
14. Harold, playwright responsible for the film "Betrayal" (6)
15. Annette, actress in "The American President" (6)
18. How many "Flew over the Cuckoo's Nest"? (3)
20. Study Film at University and you'll have to sit one (4)
21. "The . . . . that Time Forgot" (1974) (4)
23. Here inside are found horse-straps used in
    cowboy films (5)
24. Change icy trek for type of staircase in ghost films (7)
25. Freddie Bartholomew played "Little Lord
    . . . ." (10)

Down

1. Batman's waddling adversary played by Danny DeVito (7)
2. Type of Jump – "of Faith" made by Steve Martin (4)
3. James Coburn movie: "Harry . . . . . . Pocket"
   (1973) (2 & 4)
4. One of the voices behind the "Toy Story" characters (3 & 5)
5. Spike Lee's "Do the . . . . . Thing" – Not wrong (5)
6. Children's fantasy: "The Indian in . . . ." (3 & 8)
7. Odd 24 hour periods for Ralph Fiennes sci-fi film (7 & 4)
13. Wolfgang, director of "Das Boot"/"The Boat" (1981) (8)
16. I am grey– turned over for movie's sights and symbols (7)
17. Stan, English comedian who was partner to
    Oliver Hardy (6)
19. A Nile reversal for "Amateur" actress, Ms. Lowensohn (5)
22. The Oscar conceals a visible memory of a wound (4)

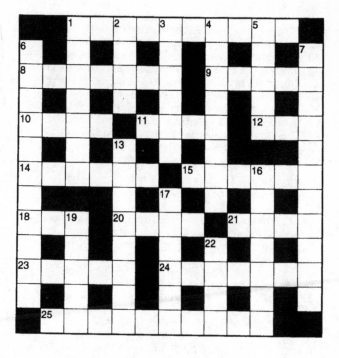

Across

1. "Apollo 13" is about . . . . . nauts in peril (5)
4. ". . . . . Along the Mohawk" – musical instruments you beat (5)
10. High musical form which includes "Porgy and Bess" (5)
11. "The . . . ." 1984 Robert Redford movie (7)
12. Metal shapes worn by sheriffs in Westerns (3 & 5)
13. Magazines ask readers to . . . . for their favourite film (4)
15. The sailing in some movies conceals what's troubling you (6)
17. Nationality of "Hamlet" whom Olivier played on film (6)
19. Lounge around with first four letters of 16 Down? (4)
20. Role for which Christopher Reeve achieved most fame (8)
23. John Boorman directed movie: "Beyond . . . ." (7)
24. Short form of Angela as played by Geena Davis (5)
25. Bob, singer, acted in "Pat Garrett and Billy the Kid" (5)
26. Bing Crosby film: "The . . . . . of St. Mary's" (5)

Down

2. Serious-sounding surname of "Home Alone" actor, Daniel (5)
3. "You're acting in movie" – hides responding to stimulus (8)
5. Kind of rodents featured in film "Willard" (4)
6. Rumours mar icon – changing him into early name in radio (7)
7. Eric Cantona/Bobby Moore have made films, but as what were they better known? (11)
8. Sidney Lumet's 1957 courtroom drama – "Twelve . . . . . Men" (5)
9. Roy Scheider helicopter thriller (1983) (4 & 7)
14. Light coloured visage for Bob Hope's comedy Western? (8)
16. George, actor who played James Bond only once (7)
18. Humorous; Jerry Lewis appeared in the film ". . . . . Bones" (5)
21. An Indian emperor or filmworld bigwig (5)
22. "No value at cinema?" – hiding brief, bright star (4)

**COMING SOON
TO A BOOKSHOP
NEAR YOU
MANY MORE
THOMAS TRICKETT
CROSSWORD
TITLES**

THE
END

SOLUTIONS

Crossword No. 1.

ACROSS. 1 Rendezvous 8 Address 9 Cat On 10 Ever
11 Toto 12 Ail 14 Fiddle 15 Wilde's 18 Raj 20 Troy 21 Year
23 Allah 24 Rampage 25 Secrets And

DOWN. 1 Redhead 2 Need 3 Euston 4 Victoria 5 Ultra
6 James Ferman 7 On Elm Street 13 Fletcher 16 Die Hard
17 Poirot 19 Julie 22 Emma

Crossword No. 2.

ACROSS. 1 Scope 4 Dance 10 Rouse 11 Othello
12 Scheider 13 Buck 15 Berlin 17 Besson 19 Rick
20 Haunting 23 Erasers 24 Floor 25 Adult 26 Frisk

DOWN. 2 Couch 3 Presidio 5 Ashy 6 Colours
7 Pressburger 8 Honey 9 Working Girl 14 Jennifer
16 Rock And 18 Cause 21 Irons 22 Bell

Crossword No. 3.

ACROSS. 1 Beaches 7 Steel 8 Actress 9 Bridge 11 Guess
13 Hook 14 Inferno 15 Gere 16 Brief 17 As Time 21 Neville
22 Agony 23 Burgess

DOWN. 2 Encounters 3 Christie 4 Elsa 5 Star 6 Dead
9 Barry 10 Goodfellas 12 Afore 13 Hoarding 18 Toga
19 Mini 20 Menu

Crossword No. 4.

ACROSS. 1 Larry 7 Stallone 8 Shots 10 St.Trinians
12 Enter The 14 Odin 16 Brad 17 Striking 20 Roger Vadim
23 Davis 24 American 25 Sheen

DOWN 1 Leslie 2 Rats 3 Star 4 Blink 5 Tom And Viv
6 Neeson 9 Story 11 Strangler 13 Hit 15 Vivid 16 Barman
18 Gibson 19 Brain 21 Alas 22 M*A*S*H

Crossword No. 5.

ACROSS. 6 Attenborough 8 Torpedo 9 Theta 10 Olin
12 Balsam 14 Loren 15 Hagman 16 Cast 19 Redig
21 Sawalha 22 Four Weddings

DOWN 1 Sterling 2 Sneer 3 Motor 4 Postman 5 Ague
6 Action Hero 7 Dalmatians 11 Son 12 Beg 13 Stallone
14 Langtry 17 Askey 18 Swede 20 Drop

Crossword No. 6.

ACROSS. 3 Manhattan 8 Evan 9 Birdcage 10 Hassle
13 Ernie 14 Tequila 15 Set 16 Earache 17 Flesh 21 Cancer
22 Accident 23 Juan 24 Orchestra

DOWN. 1 Verhoeven 2 Cassandra 4 Abbey 5 Harriet 6 Tuck
7 Alga 11 Wives Club 12 Katharine 14 Tee 15 Shivers
18 Actor 19 Scar 20 Wish

Crossword No. 7.

ACROSS.1 Lieutenant 8 Artists 9 Tamed 10 Noel 11 Hero
12 D.O.A. 14 Foster 15 Called 18 Cat 20 Ahab 21 Emma
23 Notre 24 Deplore 25 Uma Thurman

DOWN. 1 Letters 2 Elsa 3 Taster 4 National 5 Nomad
6 Magnificent 7 Edward, James 13 Red Alert 16 Lampoon
17 Landau 19 Tatum 22 Spam

Crossword No. 8.

ACROSS. 1 Oscar 4 Stone 10 On Air 11 Stretch
12 Napoleon 13 Trek 15 Iguana 17 Dallas 19 Loot
20 Maclaine 23 Rain Man 24 Under 25 Entry 26 Vicar

DOWN. 2 Stamp 3 Airplane 5 Torn 6 Natural
7 Born Killers 8 Ascot 9 Shakespeare 14 Paul Muni
16 Utopian 18 Saint 21 India 22 Emir

Crossword No. 9.

ACROSS.1 Swimmer 7 Boyle 8 Poitier 9 Splash 11 Debra
13 Fate 14 Arizona 15 Duel 16 Story 17 Bedlam 21 Brosnan
22 Scott 23 Robards

DOWN.2 Whorehouse 3 Maternal 4 Exes 5 Soup 6 Plea
9 Simon 10 Sutherland 12 Minim 13 Fantasia 18 Duck
19 Alto 20 Trio

Crossword No. 10.

ACROSS. 1 Spock 7 Beatrice 8 Lewis 10 Paul McGann
12 Hathaway 14 Dogs 16 Oven 17 Accident 20 Washington
23 Niven 24 Landings 25 Terms

DOWN.1 Splash 2 Clip 3 Hell 4 Stack 5 Lisa Bonet
6 Dennis 9 Satan 11 Streisand 13 Arc 15 Nixon 16 Orwell
18 Tennis 19 Vigil 21 Gigi 22 Nile

Crossword No. 11.

ACROSS. 6 Ewan McGregor 8 Inherit 9 Gable 10 Shaw
12 Ransom 14 Green 15 Oberon 16 Mann 19 Three
21 Tonight 22 Bonham Carter

DOWN.1 Bathgate 2 Emery 3 I Get A 4 Bergman 5 Comb
6 Eric Stoltz 7 Terminator 11 Urn 12 Red 13 Stargate
14 Gone The 17 Stump 18 Inlay 20 Riot

Crossword No. 12.

ACROSS. 3 Barbarian 8 Exam 9 Sarandon 10 Signal
13 Oprah 14 Arizona 15 Rik 16 Thunder 17 Sands
21 Retain 22 Portrait 23 Knee 24 Valentino

DOWN. 1 Get Shorty 2 Dangerous 4 Aisle 5 Berserk
6 Rent 7 Atom 11 Mountains 12 Passenger 14 Air
15 Redraft 18 Orton 19 Iona 20 Stye

Crossword No. 13.

ACROSS. 1 Salma Hayek 8 Leagues 9 Sweet 10 Cock
11 Weir 12 Yen 14 Blithe 15 Safari 18 Art 20 Paul 21 Kids
23 Tiara 24 Soprano 25 Encounters

DOWN. 1 Scacchi 2 Loud 3 Austen 4 Austrian 5 Enemy
6 Black Beauty 7 Stan Winston 13 The Piano 16 Animals
17 Hudson 19 Train 22 Epée

Crossword No. 14.

ACROSS. 1 Hammy 4 Fritz 10 Alien 11 Amateur
12 A Man Of No 13 Ward 15 Newman 17 Curtis 19 Role
20 Isabella 23 Weekend 24 Niner 25 O'Shea 26 A Star

DOWN. 2 Anita 3 Man Woman 5 Road 6 The Last 7 Dana
Andrews 8 Paint 9 Fred Astaire 14 Husbands 16 Walters
18 Aside 21 Lanza 22 Here

Crossword No. 15.

ACROSS. 1 Stewart 7 Elmer 8 Beatles 9 Zanuck 11 Terry
13 Tess 14 October 15 Halo 16 Evils 17 Edward 21 Garland
22 Davis 23 Bananas

DOWN. 2 The Leopard 3 Waterloo 4 Reed 5 Flea 6 Beau
9 Zorba 10 Casablanca 12 Stand 13 Travolta 18 Wray
19 Rain 20 Baba

Crossword No. 16.

ACROSS. 1 Hands 7 Homeward 8 Noose 10 Highlander
12 Marching 14 Reds 16 Clan 17 Lee Evans 20 Oscar
Wilde 23 Adieu 24 Castaway 25 Basil

DOWN 1 Hansom 2 Dish 3 Moth 4 Texas 5 Handlebar
6 Adores 9 Eight 11 Broadcast 13 Née 15 Zenda 16 Choice
18 Sequel 19 Cream 21 Iran 22 Edna

Crossword No. 17.

ACROSS. 6 Charing Cross 8 Tin Drum 9 Cargo 10 Yobs 12 Recall 14 Peron 15 Yellow 16 Sexy 19 Overt 21 Sabrina 22 Lauren Bacall

DOWN. 1 Cannibal 2 Nitro 3 A Game 4 Bracken 5 Tsar 6 Cathy Tyson 7 Volleyball 11 New 12 Rod 13 American 14 Posters 17 A Song 18 A Bear 20 Edam

Crossword No. 18.

ACROSS. 3 Spitfires 8 Teas 9 True Lies 10 Arrows 13 Games 14 Heroine 15 Par 16 Rerides 17 Dafoe 21 Horror 22 Anjelica 23 Mona 24 Tennessee

DOWN. 1 Strangers 2 Barrymore 4 Patsy 5 Thumper 6 Idle 7 Eden 11 Mia Farrow 12 Rehearsal 14 Has 15 Perkins 18 Shane 19 Anne 20 Kern

Crossword No. 19.

ACROSS. 1 Brainstorm 8 Insects 9 Irish 10 View 11 Falk 12 Zak 14 Reilly 15 Angels 18 Tit 20 City 21 Acre 23 Nolte 24 Plotter 25 Sam Shepard

DOWN. 1 Buscemi 2 Arch 3 Nassau 4 Thinking 5 Reisz 6 Silverstone 7 Shakespeare 13 Slickers 16 Excited 17 Staple 19 Talia 22 Coma

Crossword No. 20.

ACROSS. 1 Smash 4 Tramp 10 Disco 11 Deborah 12 Alcatraz 13 Limb 15 Desert 17 Mating 19 Upon 20 Farewell 23 Narrate 24 On The 25 Zebra 26 Stone

DOWN. 2 Music 3 Scooters 5 Ruby 6 Martini 7 Edward Burns 8 J. Dean 9 The Big Sleep 14 Barefoot 16 Scourge 18 Bates 21 Elton 22 Hair

Crossword No. 21.

ACROSS. 1 Patriot 7 Nimoy 8 Coppola 9 Reagan 11 Garbo
13 Apes 14 Ian Holm 15 Epic 16 Front 17 Nelson
21 Mitchum 22 Royce 23 Thin Man

DOWN. 2 Apocalypse 3 Republic 4 Only 5 Time 6 Kong
9 Robot 10 Ace Ventura 12 Onion 13 American 18 Lion
19 Once 20 Fish

Crossword No. 22.

ACROSS. 1 Chill 7 Victoria 8 Major 10 MacPherson
12 Travolta 14 Fred 16 John 17 Beginner 20 Gary Oldman
23 Reach 24 Excerpts 25 Motel

DOWN. 1 Cement 2 Loom 3 Limp 4 Steel 5 Armstrong
6 Damned 9 Razor 11 Bacharach 13 Tee 15 Sitar
16 Jagged 18 Rachel 19 Sorry 21 Data 22 Nero

Crossword No. 23.

ACROSS. 6 The Madness Of 8 Rioters 9 Altar 10 Eons
12 Troisi 14 Sabre 15 Listen 16 Uses 19 Nurse 21 Cilento
22 Winterbottom

DOWN 1 Heroines 2 Baker 3 Angst 4 Astaire 5 Host
6 Three Blind 7 Brainstorm 11 Wan 12 Try 13 Insanity
14 Seventh 17 Scary 18 Bloom 20 Rain

Crossword No. 24.

ACROSS. 3 John Wayne 8 Elam 9 Calamity 10 Imelda
13 On Cue 14 Bizarre 15 Cat 16 Reactor 17 On Set
21 Untrue 22 Left Foot 23 Anne 24 Cleopatra

DOWN 1 Demi Moore 2 James Caan 4 Oscar 5 No Limit
6 Army 7 Nuts 11 Armstrong 12 Gentlemen 14 Bar
15 Coppola 18 Outer 19 Hell 20 Otto

Crossword No. 25.

ACROSS. 1 After Hours 8 Russell 9 Drama 10 Cent
11 Anon 12 Mai 14 Wicker 15 Tragic 18 Leg 20 Marx
21 Year 23 Inman 24 Tresses 25 Paul McGann

DOWN. 1 Arsenic 2 Them 3 Ruling 4 Ordinary 5 Realm
6 Bruce Willis 7 David Caruso 13 Terminal 16 Gleason
17 Arctic 19 Gemma 22 Vera

Crossword No. 26.

ACROSS. 1 Alive 4 Scent 10 Robes 11 Cat's Eye
12 Of A Woman 13 As It 15 Winona 17 Brenda 19 Late
20 Rosalind 23 Eastern 24 Welch 25 Laura 26 Ryder

DOWN 2 Libra 3 Viscount 5 Cots 6 Nielsen 7 Orson Welles
8 Ocean 9 Death And The 14 Broadway 16 Natasha
18 Hound 21 I'll Be 22 Hear

Crossword No. 27.

ACROSS. 1 Alabama 7 Bites 8 Bellboy 9 Seagal 11 Store
13 Pity 14 Olivier 15 Calm 16 Smart 17 Stoker 21 Estevez
22 Seven 23 Doyenne

DOWN. 2 Lieutenant 3 Ballroom 4 Moon 5 Rice 6 Berg
9 Sheik 10 Arthur Penn 12 River 13 Premiere 18 Omen
19 Ever 20 Oslo

Crossword No. 28.

ACROSS. 1 Flash 7 Beguiled 8 Enrol 10 Waterfront
12 Scabbard 14 Barr 16 Akim 17 Pastoral 20 The Killing
23 Donat 24 Sullivan 25 Eddie

DOWN. 1 Fields 2 Slow 3 Were 4 Buffs 5 Cleopatra
6 Editor 9 Lambs 11 Farinelli 13 Rea 15 Stand 16 Artist
18 Little 19 Mimic 21 Lean 22 Gold

Crossword No. 29.

ACROSS. 6 Let's Make Love 8 Surfers 9 Polka 10 Seek
12 Pebble 14 Coeur 15 Pistol 16 Echo 19 Errol
21 October 22 New Nightmare

DOWN. 1 Starlets 2 Amber 3 A Kiss 4 Flipper 5 Evil
6 Last Supper 7 Racecourse 11 Col 12 Pun 13 Backbeat
14 Collins 17 Tough 18 State 20 Reel

Crossword No. 30.

ACROSS. 3 Armstrong 8 Even 9 Evidence 10 Frames
13 Rooms 14 Another 15 Ang 16 Outland 17 Crisp
21 Acuter 22 Fletcher 23 Jaye 24 Love In The

DOWN. 1 Jefferson 2 Belafonte 4 Reese 5 Shining
6 Reef 7 Nick 11 Christmas 12 Mrs.Parker 14 And
15 And Then 18 Darth 19 Cleo 20 It Be

Crossword No. 31.

ACROSS. 1 Under Siege 8 Hoskins 9 Smell 10 Fear
11 Bird 12 Kev 14 One Eye 15 Kramer 18 Elm
20 Eyes 21 Grit 23 Offer 24 Brennan 25 Earth Girls

DOWN. 1 Upstage 2 Dail 3 Russia 4 Insiders
5 Greek 6 The Flower Of 7 Oliver Stone 13 My Secret
16 Moranis 17 Bed Bug 19 Mafia 22 Deer

Crossword No. 32.

ACROSS. 1 A Wave 4 Steve 10 Aidan 11 Returns
12 No Way Out 13 Lira 15 Carter 17 Jacobi 19 Nude
20 Backcomb 23 O'Connor 24 Idler 25 Eddie 26 Jerry

DOWN. 2 Widow 3 Van Dyke. D. 5 Tate 6 Vertigo
7 Danny Cannon 8 Freud 9 A Star Is Born 14 Backside
16 Redford 18 Cairo 21 Oiler 22 Anti

Crossword No. 33.

ACROSS. 1 Swanson 7 Delon 8 Mitchum 9 Gloria 11 Devon
13 King 14 Advance 15 Guts 16 Class 17 Wesley
21 Caravan 22 Naked 23 Cashier

DOWN. 2 White House 3 Nicholas 4 Onus 5 Well 6 Poor
9 Glenn 10 Innerspace 12 Ivory 13 Ken Loach 18 Siam
19 Eden 20 Tara

Crossword No. 34.

ACROSS.1 Betty 7 Broccoli 8 Greer 10 Restaurant
12 Needless 14 Edge 16 Gags 17 Rampling 20 Blackbeard
23 Tiger 24 Exciting 25 Leone

DOWN. 1 Big Man 2 Tier 3 Writ 4 Scout 5 Tom And Viv
6 Little 9 Reels 11 Vengeance 13 Spa 15 Sport 16 Goblet
18 George 19 Skate 21 Erne 22 Dime

Crossword No. 35.

ACROSS. 6 Director's Cut 8 Suspect 9 Hunch 10 Lola
12 Alison 14 Faint 15 Sorrow 16 Imam 19 Resat 21 Captain
22 Robert Altman

DOWN. 1 Wrestler 2 Screw 3 Youth 4 Asphalt 5 Burn
6 Disclosure 7 Phenomenon 11 Law 12 Any 13 Sam Raimi
14 Forties 17 Scott 18 Apple 20 Stop

Crossword No. 36.

ACROSS. 3 Joan Allen 8 Arch 9 Electric 10 Killer 13 Visit
14 Surreal 15 Pal 16 Clooney 17 China 21 Ranger
22 Sneakers 23 Mars 24 Tarantino

DOWN. 1 Malkovich 2 Eccleston 4 Opera 5 Needful 6 Lute
7 Erik 11 Hemingway 12 Albatross 14 Say 15 Perfect
18 Arson 19 Anna 20 Java

Crossword No. 37.

ACROSS. 1 Redemption 8 Ecstasy 9 Other 10 Ices
11 Whip 12 Act 14 Silent 15 To Garp 18 All 20 Exit 21 Hair
23 Eddie 24 Burmese 25 Dartagnan's

DOWN. 1 Russell 2 Dial 3 May The 4 Thompson 5 O'Shea
6 Kevin Spacey 7 Prêt-à-Porter 13 Indecent 16 Amadeus
17 Kitbag 19 Lydia 22 Aria

Crossword No. 38.

ACROSS. 1 Mouse 4 Pluto 10 Opera 11 Passage
12 Atlantic 13 Spiv 15 DeNiro 17 Grodin 19 Hush 20
Campbell 23 Loretta 24 Ozone 25 Flynn 26 Rebel

DOWN. 2 O'Neal 3 Scanners 5 Lost 6 Trapped
7 Cop And A Half 8 April 9 Lee Van Cleef 14 Drop Zone
16 Nostril 18 Japan 21 Elope 22 Stun

Crossword No. 39.

ACROSS. 1 A Serial 7 Hired 8 Barbara 9 Spirit 11 Lenny
13 Dust 14 Odyssey 15 Caan 16 Caine 17 Shower
21 Vatican 22 False 23 The Easy

DOWN. 2 Stagecoach 3 Robinson 4 Aura 5 Pimp 6 Fear
9 Swash 10 Insomniacs 12 By Air 13 Dynamite 18 Oban
19 Easy 20 Wash

Crossword No. 40.

ACROSS. 1 Bilko 7 Crawford 8 Truss 10 Specialist
12 Minnelli 14 Bald 16 Easy 17 Butcher's 20 Tim Robbins
23 Siren 24 The Birds 25 Belly

DOWN. 1 Bottom 2 Kiss 3 Eric 4 Swear 5 Nominated
6 Edited 9 Speed 11 One Summer 13 Lou 15 Icons
16 Estate 18 Sydney 19 Boris 21 Beds 22 Side

Crossword No. 41.

ACROSS. 6 Brian DePalma 8 Retsina 9 Tango 10 Open
12 Lemmon 14 Wiser 15 Unseen 16 Quin 19 Craft
21 Theatre 22 The River Wild

DOWN. 1 Mistress 2 Antic 3 He-Man 4 Panther 5 Oman
6 Bertolucci 7 Sonnenfeld 11 Tin 12 Leo 13 Mountain
14 Western 17 Steve 18 Heart 20 Ache

Crossword No. 42.

ACROSS. 3 The People 8 Amok 9 Twin Town 10 Coyote
13 Laugh 14 Berkoff 16 Nervous 17 Larry 21 Recede
22 Homicide 23 Lair 24 Young Guns

DOWN. 1 Barcelona 2 Bodyguard 4 Hotel 5 Poitier 6 Oats
7 Lawn 11 Courtenay 12 Of My Heart 14 Bus 15 Funding
18 Green 19 Solo 20 Lion

Crossword No. 43.

ACROSS. 1 Disclosure 8 Altered 9 Sugar 10 Etch 11 Here
12 Rea 14 Disney 15 States 18 Owl 20 Need 21 Dern
23 Aisle 24 Absolve 25 French Kiss

DOWN. 1 Detects 2 Sore 3 Ladder 4 Suspects 5 Roger
6 James Doohan 7 Bryan Singer 13 Sean Bean 16 Thewlis
17 Rehash 19 Loser 22 Asti

Crossword No. 44.

ACROSS. 1 Bobby 4 Melba 10 Idaho 11 Compose
12 L. Jackson 13 Ahoy 15 Rocky's 17 Maoris 19 Kick
20 Palme D'Or 23 Sunrise 24 Spike 25 Straw 26 Snake

DOWN. 2 O'Hara 3 Brooklyn 5 Emma 6 Brother
7 Killer's Kiss 8 Actor 9 Meryl Streep 14 Parmesan
16 Coconut 18 Dated 21 Drink 22 Gina

Crossword No. 45.

ACROSS.1 Batman's 7 Bacon 8 In A Kilt 9 Crabbe 11 Sally
13 Park 14 Vertigo 15 Shoe 16 Harry 17 Brooks 21 Russell
22 Glory 23 Admiral

DOWN. 2 Anne Archer 3 Make Love 4 Nell 5 Fair 6 Cobb
9 Chris 10 Barbarella 12 Brats 13 Polanski
18 Only 19 Kurt 20 Budd

Crossword No. 46.

ACROSS.1 Helps 7 Cowgirls 8 Round 10 Kieslowski
12 Guinness 14 I Die 16 Pale 17 Lawrence 20 Linda Blair
23 Naked 24 Operator 25 Tears

DOWN. 1 Herzog 2 Pink 3 Dogs 4 A Good 5 President
6 Aspire 9 Diana 11 Dillinger 13 Sea 15 Train 16 Pillow
18 Exodus 19 Sarah 21 Look 22 Rage

Crossword No. 47.

ACROSS. 6 Deborah Harry 8 Vainest 9 Bleep 10 Drip
12 Weasel 14 Anger 15 Ignore 16 Berg 19 Elbow
21 Epaulet 22 Four Weddings

DOWN. 1 Oblivion 2 Green 3 White 4 Gambler 5 Free
6 David Niven 7 Applegates 11 One 12 Wet 13 Stealing
14 Artwork 17 Fever 18 Candy 20 Blow

Crossword No. 48.

ACROSS. 3 Surviving 8 Hood 9 Hardcore 10 Insane
13 Trout 14 Stylist 15 Say 16 Accused 17 Eagle 21 Eaters
22 Ridicule 23 Alan 24 Val Kilmer

DOWN. 1 Christian 2 Hopscotch 4 Usher 5 Variety 6 Vice
7 Nark 11 Minghella 12 Streisand 14 Sad 15 Seagull
18 Geese 19 Viva 20 Mink

Crossword No. 49.

ACROSS. 1 Palminteri 8 Hungary 9 Might 10 Chum
11 Bull 12 Tea 14 Pinter 15 Bening 18 One
20 Exam 21 Land 23 Reins 24 Rickety 25 Fauntleroy

DOWN. 1 Penguin 2 Leap 3 In Your 4 Tim Allen 5 Right
6 The Cupboard 7 Strange Days 13 Petersen 16 Imagery
17 Laurel 19 Elina 22 Scar

Crossword No. 50.

ACROSS. 1 Astro 4 Drums 10 Opera 11 Natural
12 Tin Stars 13 Vote 15 Ailing 17 Danish 19 Laze
20 Superman 23 Rangoon 24 Angie 25 Dylan 26 Bells

DOWN. 2 Stern 3 Reacting 5 Rats 6 Marconi 7 Footballers
8 Angry 9 Blue Thunder 14 Paleface 16 Lazenby 18 Funny
21 Mogul 22 Nova

The Thomas Trickett Series
Purchasing Enquiries

In connection with the purchase of any
titles in the Thomas Trickett series please
contact the Information Desk on 01202 397379
or write to I.P. Llewellyn, Managing Director,
Thomas Trickett Publications Ltd
4 Harrison Avenue, Bournemouth BH1 4NT, England

AUTOGRAPHS OR NOTES